THE HOUSE ON PRAGUE STREET

THE HOUSE ON PRAGUE STREET

HANA DEMETZ

Translated from the German
by the author

ST. MARTIN'S PRESS
NEW YORK

Library of Congress Cataloging in Publication Data

Demetz, Hana.
The house on Prague street.

Translation of Ein Haus in Böhmen. I. Title
PZ4.D3777Ho   [PT2664.E44]   833'.914   79-27312
ISBN 0-312-39322-9

For Ruth Hein

I still have dreams about the old house. I can see everything quite clearly: the three steps leading to the glass veranda, the yellow front door with its brass trim, the hallway where every step resounded even if I walked on tiptoe. In every dream I walk up the stairs. Between the first and second floors the stairs are covered in red-and-yellow plush, and there is a flowerpot on every step: asparagus fern, umbrella trees, and cactus. The red-and-yellow plush carpet runs to the bedroom doors of the second floor, but I, in my dream, climb on.

Now the stairs are no longer carpeted, the windows are smaller, and the door to which I am drawn is narrow and made of iron. In my dream I open it. Hot dry attic air presses on me, my eyes have not yet penetrated the semidarkness. It takes a while before I can make out the familiar shapes: the old steamer trunks and the rocking horse, the armoire with the yellowed photographs, the four-poster with red velvet cushions, my great-great-grandfather's rickety handcart, the old-fashioned bicycle. It is very quiet here; only far below somewhere in the street, there is the rattle of a car. The world is far away. I snuggle into the friendly semidarkness, smell the fragrance of the dry brick floor and of the roof beams, see the light blue squares of the skylights above me. And in my dream I am happy.

My mother and her two sisters grew up in the old house. My mother was the eldest. Zdena, the middle sister, had been a twin, but her little brother was born dead. It took my grandfather a long time before he forgave my grandmother this dead son. As if it had been her fault! But my grandfather was a very strict man. The youngest daughter, Ella, was born many years later.

The old house stood at the edge of the public park. It had a huge garden, and its rear wall was painted black. Two crossed hammers were painted in white on the black surface above the lettering, also in white: *Max Löwy, Coal and Transport*. Why my grandfather had decided to display the sign on the back of his house I do not know; perhaps he believed in subtle advertising. The offices and the wholesale coal firm were closer to town, behind the old garden, and my grandfather only had to stroll through the grounds and through the garden gate to get to his office. But usually he preferred going around the house in order to be seen on his walk to work and to be greeted by all his acquaintances and friends. He liked to be seen and acknowledged.

My mother and her sisters did not have a long walk to school; the local high school was at the other side of the park. My mother often told me how she had envied her classmates who lived far away and were permitted to stay in the classroom at lunchtime and drink lukewarm coffee from soda bottles. But my grandfather would never have allowed his daughters to bring lukewarm coffee in soda bottles for their lunch, even if they had lived a long way away from school.

The business had been founded by my grandfather's grandfather. He had come to the small town from Prague shortly after the Austrian Emperor signed the law permitting Jews to move out of the ghettos. He had arrived with his wife and with his son and with a small handcart: a stooped, shy man with a long beard, wearing a black coat and hat. His only other possession was his good name; he was one of the many grandsons of the famous Rabbi Löw and therefore belonged to one of the most illustrious Jewish families in central Europe. The handcart he had brought from Prague to the small town became the first transport van. Still wearing his black coat and hat, he would drag the cart to a farm, from the farm to the flour mill, from the flour mill to the shop, and back to the farm again. For many years he wandered, his eyes lowered and his arms crossed behind his back, the strap of the cart slung over his shoulder. His back grew even more bent and his face became gray with the dust of many country roads. But when he died, his son could afford to buy a horse and a second-hand carriage, and there was even money enough for a respectable plot in the small Jewish cemetery.

This son, my great-grandfather, did not have to breathe the dust of the country roads. He did not even drive the carriage himself for long, because he understood about business. Soon he employed one driver, then two, and by the time he took a wife and his son, my grandfather, was born, there were three pairs of horses in the stable and a shop sign.

As the years went by, my great-grandfather had five more sons and three daughters, and as his family grew, the reputation of his business grew as well. The stables and the storage rooms were enlarged every year, and more land was bought. My great-grandfather built the house on Prague Street, a two-story structure with a huge kitchen and many rooms and thick walls intended to shelter many generations. My great-grandfather was proud of his name and dreamed of an important future for his family. He became one of the most respectable citizens of the town. He died of a heart attack at sixty, after he had slapped one of his drivers who had not been polite enough with a customer. The very same driver then bore my great-grandfather's coffin to the family gravesite, with the mayor, the doctor, and the town councilor as the pallbearers.

My grandfather, the oldest son, inherited the business. He also inherited his father's temper, his bushy black eyebrows, and the high forehead that turned red at every angry outburst. Across his waistcoat he wore the thick gold watchchain his father had worn; he did not like the heavy watch, however, and always left it lying on his night table. Whenever my grandmother engaged a new maid, she always remembered to mention that the watch, fully wound, must remain in one particular spot on the marble tabletop any time of day or night.

When my grandfather took over the business, he paid off his brothers and told them where to settle and whom to marry. He found proper husbands for his sisters and took care to give them good dowries. He built a new warehouse and started coal deliveries, bringing new prosperity to the business. He laid out the big garden. His father's interests had still been limited to business and family; my grandfather was ready to think of the town where he was at home, and of his own place in it. He built a hostel for his drivers in the square; later it became the town's first hotel. He started a choral society, and when they performed operas, he would always take the bass role. He had the park laid out between the old house and the town school. And he had himself, his wife, and his daughters taken off the roster of the Israelite congregation. "We belong here, to this town," said my grandfather. "What good can it do us to be Jews here?"

My grandmother was a gentle, quiet woman. My grandfather had married her for her gentle, quiet ways, since he had no need to marry for money. She had not been an advantageous match. In the little mountain village that was her home she had eight brothers and sisters, and her father, the village tailor, did more patching than tailoring. But my grandmother's kindness made up a hundredfold for her lack of a dowry. She ran the large house with a friendly hand, often accomplishing more with a gentle word than her husband could with his rages. The maids and the drivers all adored her. She was tall, not beautiful, with large blue eyes that were always serious, even when she smiled. She always wore a black velvet ribbon around her slender neck.

When the First World War came it shook the peaceful life of the town a little. One of the drivers became a soldier in Serbia and was never heard of again. In the mornings there were lines in front of the bakery, and when the bread was finally doled out, it was black and seeded with corn kernels. One of my grandmother's brothers died in a burning airplane somewhere over the Vosges Mountains, giving his life for his Kaiser and his fatherland.

But the four years passed like a bad dream, and in the fall my grandfather took the train to Prague to represent the town at the arrival of the president of the new republic. He came back with enthusiasm in his eyes and a red, white, and blue button in the lapel of his Sunday suit. A portrait of President

Masaryk hung in the hall from that day on—a kindly, clever man with a white beard.

My grandfather was proud of his ability to move with the times. He was first in town to acquire a radio, and for months the town's prominent citizens would sit in his parlor night after night, earphones over their heads, arms folded across their stomachs, listening to the new sounds. His car was admired by all the residents long before the noise of all the others began to fill the streets. And when my mother and her younger sister Zdena finished school, they were sent to Prague to live with their uncle the banker. He was to let them work in his bank; my grandfather had decided that his two daughters should earn their own living instead of sitting at home busying themselves with parties and frivolities.

But the two girls did not lead a life of self-denial, filled only with office work. Prague in the twenties was a shining metropolis, and the photographs of my mother from those days showed a beautiful girl in party dress and dance gowns, with ropes of pearls that dangled amusingly almost to her knees, her pretty legs in silk stockings crossed just a bit teasingly.

My grandfather surely could not have liked the frivolous life his daughters were leading in the big city. But it had been his idea to send them to Prague, and he was not a man to go back on his own plans. He began to communicate extensively with a certain family in Königgrätz, and he watched the son of that family thoroughly and critically. Would he be good enough to marry his eldest daughter and later take over the business?

The people from Königgrätz did their best to make the decision easy for him—of course it would be an honor to marry into the family of the Löwys, an honor all around. And after grandfather had made his decision, he informed his daughter. He broke the news to her gently, because he loved his firstborn. He was gentle, but he was firm. Then the unexpected happened. For the first time in his life my grandfather found himself facing opposition. His oldest daughter did not agree with him. His oldest daughter barely knew the young man from Königgrätz. In any case, she would not let anyone tell her whom to marry. Never.

My grandfather did not believe his ears. But because he loved his firstborn, he proceeded with caution. Of course she would do what her father expected of her, he thought. The good life in Prague had made her headstrong, that's all. But when it came right down to it, she was his daughter, and he himself had never been one to give blind obedience. You really could not blame a girl for wanting to know her future husband: times had changed; we were living in a republic now; girls wanted to have their say, too. He was not a savage. He would not stand in the way of two young people wanting to meet each other. He invited the family from Königgrätz to come for coffee on Sunday afternoon.

But his daughter refused to do the honors. She locked herself in her room—let the company come and go—and said again: never! My grandfather's patience finally gave out, and the house cringed under the load of his anger. These modern ideas! These whims! Such rudeness! Who did the girl think she was? Was she trying to turn him into a laughingstock?

As always, my grandmother tried to smooth matters over. Gently she talked to my grandfather about the patience required in dealing with unreasonable children. Softly she reminded my mother of filial obedience. But neither grandfather's anger nor my grandmother's gentle admonitions could convince my mother. She only said, over and over: never!

Then frightful news reached my grandfather. The uncle from Prague reported that a certain lawyer, Prochaska, was one of my mother's most devoted admirers and that he might very well be the reason for all this upset. Again the house shook with the force of my grandfather's rage. Grandfather ordered my mother's things to be brought from Prague, and he swore that never again would he let his daughters out of his sight. What did his daughter need young Prague lawyers for? A dutiful son from the Bohemian provinces was not good enough for her?

Poor grandfather—he still did not know the whole truth. He did not know that reality would surpass even the uncle's hints. Lawyer Prochaska was Czech at least, and he had his own law firm. But my mother, she was in love with his clerk, a young man with five semesters of law, she was in love with a German student whose knowledge of Czech barely sufficed to let him pronounce her name. My mother was determined to marry this young German student, that one and no one else, even if she had to wait for him to the end of her days.

Poor grandfather. His world collapsed. His forehead paled, and he covered himself with his anger like a heavy cloak. For days he did not leave his room. Everyone began to worry about his health. They remembered the angry blow that had already caused one death. And they reminded each other how much my grandfather was like his own father. Nobody dared to speak aloud, the drivers cursed only in whispers, the maids stopped singing. My grandfather and my mother did not speak to each other. Grief lay over the house like a heavy shadow. Grandmother wept for days, for weeks. Then my mother packed her things again and left for Prague, without saying goodbye.

Grandfather gave up the fight. The following autumn he allowed his wife and his younger daughters to attend my mother's wedding in Prague. He himself did not come, and he did not forgive my mother until I was born. When I was three years old, he met my father for the first time.

My father was tall, slim, blond, and blue-eyed, and photographs of him in lieutenant's uniform always delighted my girlfriends because he looked cool and proud and still a bit dreamy.

His own people also cut all ties with him when they heard whom he was planning to marry. A Czech girl, a wealthy Jewess for a daughter-in-law, must have been even harder to bear for the family of a small official in the German part of Bohemia than the German son-in-law for my grandfather. But in contrast to my grandfather, whose heart began to melt when I made my arrival, the family in the Sudetenland remained hard. No grandchild could soften their feelings. For many years my father's people would pretend that they had no son and no brother. Only much later, when they had already sided with the mighty, did they remember the lost son and try to convince him that a divorce was essential.

In the beginning my grandmother sent money every month, in secret, because my father was still at the university and earned almost nothing. When he married he had to abandon his dream of a law office of his own. After taking his bar exams, he joined the civil service.

My parents spent the early years of their married life in many furnished rooms in many Bohemian small towns. Young government officials were transferred almost every quarter and had to go where the state sent them. Only after I was born did the civil service take pity. My father was transferred to eastern Czechoslovakia and could set up housekeeping there.

We lived in a brown house on School Street. The house was the only two-story building far and wide, not counting the school building itself, which had three stories. Behind our backyard there was another row of small houses and then the brook, which ran mud-colored and swift and which would sometimes, in the spring, creep all the way up to the back doors. On the other bank stood the town washhouse, which usually served as a hiding place for children's games, and behind it there were only meadows. The first floor of our house was occupied by the two elderly Paskud sisters, Miss Anna and Miss Sidonie. They were both teachers, and neither had ever grown to full size; everything about them was tiny. A slightly rancid smell always hovered in the hallway in front of their apartment and clung to the ladies themselves.

Our apartment was on the second floor; it had a dining room, a bedroom, a nursery, and a kitchen. Every night the folding cot would be set up for Franziska in the kitchen. Franziska, the maid, had been sent by my grandmother, also in secret, to make my mother's life easier. She came from a mountain village in northern Bohemia, and our Moravian small town, where everyone spoke a dialect she did not understand, must have seemed like wicked Babylon to her. In the brownish photographs that showed her pushing my pram, she always looked round-cheeked and slightly baffled.

I was a thin, sickly child, floating between mysterious fevers and assorted childhood diseases. My mother's face was always bent anxiously over my white metal crib. Once, returning from a Sunday picnic, my father carried me home on his back. I clung to his neck and cried and moaned because all at once I could no longer move my head. I was not quite three years old; with each of his steps there was a horrible pounding inside me, unbearably hot. It was polio.

After that, I was burning up with fever, the white metal crib turned into a prison, I screamed because I could not see my mother, I could feel her hands, but I could not see her.

Six months later I was able to get out of bed, but I had forgotten how to walk, and my right leg had forgotten how to grow. It was shorter. My mother's eyes filled with tears, she held me tight and said, "Maybe this is the punishment." But then my grandfather arrived, and he was not angry any more. He kissed my father, and my father kissed his hand, and both acted embarrassed and shy.

My grandfather had brought two doctors with him, and he brought in every doctor in town. They measured me and had me do exercises. I had to drag myself across parquet floors on my knees, twenty times around the room every day; I had to lie on a table with my back up in the air and do sit-ups, twenty times in a row, mornings and evenings; I had to sleep in a plaster-cast cradle, to keep my spine straight. I screamed and fought and had nosebleeds all the time, but my right leg started to grow again. It grew and caught up with the left except for two-tenths of an inch, and I did not become a cripple.

The time came when I had had every single one of the childhood diseases; there were no more to get. I began to blossom. I made friends and gave orders through the fence at the back of the garden. First there was the pale Georgie Kitchner from next door, then the grubby girl Ernestine, who constantly wiped her runny nose on her coat sleeve. And there was even wild Rudi, ignoring my orders but nevertheless trying to drag me into the darkness of the washhouse. Even before I entered first grade I had my faithful following, I reigned with an iron hand near the brook and in the meadows, and even Rudi sometimes succumbed to my tyranny. Franziska the maid would shake her head in disapproval as she bleached our sheets in the meadow. She preferred me to go to the park with her; I would have to wear white cotton gloves and walk obediently along the pebbled paths. The military band in green uniforms would play in the circular pavilion, and poor Franziska could not take her eyes off the trumpet player who blew his horn so soulfully.

I always spent my summer vacations with my grandparents in the old house on Prague Street. The train trip to Bohemia took a whole day. Usually Franziska and I went ahead right after school finished. My parents had a vacation of their own and followed later.

Grandfather usually rode several train stops ahead to meet us, and I could spend the last leg of the long journey sitting on his knees, pulling at his bushy eyebrows and examining the golden chain which held little golden cigar clippers instead of a watch. At the final station, where cheerful baskets full of begonias hung over the platforms, there waited grandfather's gleaming Škoda car which had once been the first car in town, and old Wenzel, whose face was equally shiny. Then we drove at parade speed through the town, my grandfather waving and greeting everyone, pointing to me. It was important for the whole town to know that the Löwys' grandchild had come to stay that summer.

My grandmother waited in front of the house, her hands shaking as she reached for me. Grandfather grumbled, "Here we are, just don't squeeze the child too hard!" and on a table in the veranda stood a glass dish with grandfather's strawberries, the early harvest, with sugar and cream.

Then I had to inspect the gardens. Roses and phlox spread their perfume in front of the house, and peas were in bloom at the back fence. The three-cornered, veined leaves of strawberries rested on the moist earth, and at the black-painted back wall, underneath the inscription *Max Löwy, Coal and Transport,* apricots and peaches grew.

Wenzel had brought the old-fashioned lawn swing down from the attic and had repaired the seats and painted them green. There I found it, between the bed of rhubarb and the currant bushes, waiting just for me, and the small weathervane on its roof turned in the evening breeze. Grandfather lighted another cigar and said, "Just watch. When this one begins to glimmer, supper will be ready." We swung slowly, and grand-father was right: when the cigar in his hand began to glimmer red, grandmother stepped out onto the veranda, her cheeks rosy from the stove as she called us in for supper.

Franziska was sitting in the kitchen. She had not stopped talking since our arrival, and she let old Emma wait on her, because she was a guest here who wanted to be honored on her first night. In the dining room the lights were already lit, the carved flowers and fruits in the doors of the sideboard glowed bright and dark, light and shadow, and above the red plush sofa hung the portrait depicting grandfather in the matchmaker's costume from *The Bartered Bride.* Old Emma served my favorite dish, Wiener schnitzel with browned potatoes, and grandfather fed me especially tasty bites of his special salad. Only grandmother did not eat much, she smiled and patted my hand. Then we had meringues with wine sauce, but I could not manage any more food. I fell asleep and had to be carried to bed.

In the morning I helped grandfather water the currant bushes and the silver firs at the garden gate, and sometimes even the beds of carnations. The only plants I was not allowed to touch were the strawberries, because there, grandfather said, every droplet of water had to be considered.

Then grandmother took me to the office to be weighed. It was a yearly ritual: she weighed me on the first day of every vacation, because to her mind I was always too skinny and was supposed to put on weight. The figure was recorded on the office calendar, so that on the last vacation day it could be compared with another reading of the scales. And the few grams that had collected on me during the course of the summer—there was never more than that, because I was a thin child—they always made grandmother very happy. When I became older and more crafty, I would borrow small kitchen weights from old Emma, and on the last day of vacation I would hang them on a string around my waist, under my dress. I meant well and liked to see grandmother happy.

For our midmorning snack, Sonia and I and all our dolls would be served farmer's cheese mixed with sugar and egg yolks and raisins on the sunny lawn behind the house. Sonia, who was two years younger than I, lived next door. My grandfather had given her parents the land for a wedding present, because Sonia's mother was my grandfather's niece. However, grandfather had hardly expected the young couple to build a glass monstrosity, as he called it, instead of a house. It was a very modern house, with a flat roof and a huge terrace, with a winter garden and a living room into which—horrors!—one had to step down; there was also a swimming pool in the garden.

Grandfather immediately planted a hedge around his own garden, so that he would not have to look at the glass monstrosity. From that time on, he was not very kindly disposed toward Aunt Klara. But I enjoyed the neighbors and the swimming pool, and even grandmother would sometimes slip through the hedge to watch us and to pay Aunt Klara a little visit. The two women would sit under the lawn umbrella, grandmother erect in her dark dress, the black velvet ribbon around her neck, her hair smooth and white; Aunt Klara in long white linen pants—thank heavens grandfather could not see those—with her hair fashionably tousled and with the current issue of *Harper's Bazaar* on her lap. Sometimes the baby nurse in her white uniform also sat on the lawn, and Sonia's little brother would kick his little suntanned legs and rock his baby carriage this way and that.

The summer days were full of sunshine, strung together like shiny beads. When rain threatened, there was always the hope that we might be permitted to play in the attic; this promise made us both, Sonia and me, unbelievably obedient. Of course we could only play there if we had first earned such an honor.

When the time finally came, old Emma would climb cautiously ahead of us, first over red-and-yellow plush, between the flowerpots. On the second-floor landing she had to stop and catch her breath. We poked one another and giggled, because going up we had caught a glimpse of her old legs in their thick black stockings, causing us to forget the great moment for a while. But we caught ourselves when Emma shook her head, annoyed, and then we stepped gingerly over the uncarpeted stairs, holding our breath. When Emma had taken the key out of her apron pocket and unlocked the narrow iron door, we held hands, our hearts beating all the way up in our throats.

The door made a soft creaking sound as it was opened, the air came blowing toward us, hot and dry, before Emma lifted the sky lights to let in the breeze. Then she said, "Don't do anything foolish up here." Mumbling something more, she turned to go.

For a while we could hear her heavy steps on the stairs,

and then we were alone in the semidark. Sonia held my hand tightly and whispered, "Aren't you even a little bit afraid?" And of course I was not afraid, I was two years older than she. So I led her to the rocking horse, which had yellow glass eyes and a real black mane, and she forgot all about being afraid.

Next we tried out the rickety high chair and the red velvet cushions on the seats of the sleigh. Of course I had to sit in the driver's seat, and Sonia was the princess who rode with me over the seven mountains. The roof beams turned into a dark forest and the armoires turned into rocks and caves where we hid from the bad magician. We rode until we arrived at the enchanted castle, where we released the dolls who had been banished there. The four-poster with the golden tassels turned into a ballroom where we celebrated our victories, and the old baby buggy became a state coach.

At ten o'clock grandmother came and brought us our snack. She was out of breath after climbing the many stairs, and she had to sit down for a while. Quietly she watched us, her small hands folded in her lap. And then, when we begged her a lot, she carefully opened one of the chests under the eaves and showed us the treasures it held: tiny dresses that my mother and her sisters had worn, and button shoes made of black patent, and pantaloons, and yellowed lace aprons with tiers of ruffles. Another chest sheltered great-grandmother's wedding gown with its tiny waist and many satin buttons. Hanging in the armoire was grandfather's hussar uniform, complete with red trousers and shiny sabre. Great-grandmother's trousseau chest stood to one side, trimmed with strips of black iron. And behind the chests, where the roof reached all the way to the floor, rested great-great-grandfather's handcart, the shaft broken and held together with wire.

Grandmother slowly moved her hand across the worn strap of the handcart as she said, "All the things stand here together peacefully, Helenka, you see. And when your own grandchildren come up here to play, you will have to show them everything too." Her eyes were thoughtful as she spoke.

Then grandmother carefully closed the skylights because rain had begun to drum against the slanted roof, first in solitary droplets and then more and more heavily, until the attic was filled with the sound of streaming water. It ran over the roof, down it ran into the gutters, along the walls of the house it ran downward to the earth, and then, divided into many tiny streams, away, someplace, somewhere, away.

Aunt Zdena, my mother's pretty younger sister, also defied grandfather's wishes when she married. Grandfather had to accept the fact that the family from Königgrätz was not for her either. She married an executive in the bank of my uncle in Prague, and, like my mother before her, she did not worry much about grandfather's business needing a young man one day to take it over.

Grandfather took this blow with more composure than the disappointment which my mother had once caused him. He was angry for only a few days, then he allowed himself to be persuaded to attend Zdena's wedding without much protest.

Finally he concentrated all his hopes on Ella, his youngest. He was careful not to repeat the mistake that had let both his older daughters grow beyond his control. Ella was sent not to a finishing school, but to a commercial college. She was not allowed to breathe the heady air of Prague; instead, grandfather sent her to Aussig, to one of his sisters, for her practical training. Ella, the baby of the family, took it all in stride. She put on black sleeve-guards and cheerfully worked in the book-keeping rooms. She rebelled only once: when grandfather invited the people from Königgrätz for the third time, she coolly declared that she would find her own husband, should she ever decide that she needed one. The people from Königgrätz were never mentioned again, and grandfather did not even get angry.

In July, grandfather's birthday was celebrated in the old house. For weeks before, the house would be scrubbed and cleaned—secretly, because my grandfather could not stand housecleaning and the disorder it caused. Usually Franziska had to stand guard at the garden gate. As soon as grandfather turned the corner, all the pails, brooms, ladders, and even the comfortable vacuum cleaner had to disappear into the storage room. They were all pulled out again after grandfather had finished his lunchtime nap and had gone back to the office.

When the cleaning was done and the old house was polished and sparkling from top to bottom, the baking would begin. Old Emma stood her ground like a general, and the kitchen maids, Franziska, and sometimes even grandmother would be directed, instructed, and commandeered, until the fruits of all these labors began to fill the pantry shelves: cakes and tortes, breads and pastries, butter cream and apricot purée, nut crescents and chocolate fingers. The whole house was fragrant with them, and all the unsightly end pieces, crusts, and rinds found their way into Sonia's and my apron pockets and were enjoyed down to the last crumb on the sunny lawn behind the house.

Then the family began to gather; old Wenzel had to drive to the railroad station two, even three times a day. He muttered quietly to himself, because he considered it his duty to take the Škoda apart and wash it thoroughly after every trip, and on the days preceding the birthday he did not have nearly enough time.

Only the people from Warnsdorf, grandfather's two brothers and their families, arrived in their own cars, giving poor old Wenzel a chance to rest. The two brothers from Warnsdorf were mentioned often and with respect in the old house. They had added international luster to the good family name: their textile mills hummed not only in Warnsdorf but also in faraway Bucarest. My great-grandfather certainly had not dreamed that his sons would spread the name so far afield.

When the cars from Warnsdorf arrived, half of the town population would assemble in front of the old house. The two Humbers alone warranted admiration. They were a far cry from old Wenzel and grandfather's Škoda. Old Wenzel did not even wear a uniform, he had only the tattered cap with a visor. But the two chauffeurs who jumped out of the Humbers wore dashing navy blue suits adorned with double rows of silver buttons.

And the ladies! Uncle Rudolf's wife seemed to calculate each gesture as she descended from the soft leather cushions of the car. She inspected the bystanders through her lorgnette and then called for lukewarm water for her Pekinese and a glass of sherry for herself. Both were made of delicate stuff, and such a long trip did not become them at all. A large pink fan of egret feathers emerged from Uncle Fritz's car, followed by Aunt Elsa. A murmur went through the crowd every time they caught sight of the pink fan.

Once my mother caught me among the gaping crowd. My mouth stood as open as everyone else's, and my mother neatly aimed a slap on it, saying, "Don't you ever act like a poor relation!"

It was one of the rare moments when my cheerful mother seemed genuinely upset. Since that time I took care not to be present at another arrival. I could not understand what had made her so angry.

The arrival of the Warnsdorfers always brought new life to the old house. The bells Emma had fetched from the attic the day before took turns ringing from morning to night, and the Pekinese barked hoarsely all day. The two lady's maids in black dresses and tiny white aprons, who had arrived with their masters, tripped through the old house diligently and found neither Emma nor Franziska to their taste, not to mention the kitchen maids. From time to time grandfather would look very angry and would slam the doors.

The three aunts from Aussig—"the three girls," as grandmother called them—were entirely different. They would sit on the veranda with grandmother over coffee, the spoons tinkling softly in the Rosenthal cups as the aunts took turns talking. Sometimes they talked all at once, and sometimes they would giggle as if they really were young girls and not old ladies at all. Even grandmother looked very young as she sat with them. Only her eyes remained serious.

The banker uncle came from Prague with his family, but he had to stay in Aunt Klara's father's house on the square because all the bedrooms in the old house were occupied. Aunt Ella had to give up her own room and move into one of the attic bedrooms. I envied her with all my heart for being allowed to sleep so close to the attic storeroom.

Only grandfather's youngest brother, Alfred, never came. When they spoke of him, it was in whispers, with a small bourgeois shiver. He had gone all the way to Berlin with his money, had lived a wild life, had written poems and lighted his cigarettes with banknotes. In the end he had shot himself because of an actress, they said. His portrait hung in the parlor. He had without doubt been the best-looking member of the family, with dark curls and a slightly haughty expression in his blue eyes, a cigarette clasped between overly thin fingers.

On the morning of the birthday itself, the well-wishers called. The mayor of the town would come first, because he was an early riser, and would be served breakfast coffee. Then the director of the school came: he stayed a long time, drinking his glass of wine, and sighed, "Oh yes, how our youth has flown by, my dear Max!" Then the head of the hospital came for a short chat, and the gentlemen of the singing group brought a bouquet of red roses. The Councilor from the District Office kissed all the ladies' hands before he expressed his congratulations to grandfather, and grandfather would reply: "But you are not coming for my sake, my dear Joseph." The Councilor usually blushed a bright red; he was a bachelor.

The aroma of the large birthday goose came wafting in from the kitchen, the dining room table had to be pulled out to its full length, and Emma grumbled while she set it because the dinner service for twenty-four had one cracked plate, and the set of half-moon-shaped bone dishes was missing one dish entirely. Dinner was served at twelve o'clock sharp, and even the ladies from Warnsdorf were on time, although Aunt Irma looked peeved behind her lorgnette: the Pekinese was banned from the dining room on grandfather's orders. The soup with liver dumplings was a poem, said the Prague banker uncle every year, and the goose with sweet-sour red cabbage and dumplings was a true symphony. The heavy red wine served with it was a masterpiece which had been kissed by every single Muse.

Between the last bite of goose and the serving of the birthday cake I had to recite the birthday poem; the relatives clapped a lot and kissed me, and then I was allowed to blow out the birthday candles.

The gentlemen retired to the living room for coffee, and my father was questioned extensively about the frightening events that were taking place in Germany. Everyone nodded gravely and worriedly, they did not relax until grandfather passed around his cigar box saying, "Such things would be utterly impossible in this country." Then they settled back into their blue clouds of smoke.

Afternoon coffee was served in the garden. The treasures were brought from the pantry and praised, and even Aunt Irma consulted grandmother about a recipe. Only the Pekinese looked miffed and turned up his nose full of disgust when

Sonia offered him a piece of vanilla crescent. For that I
pinched his fat behind, and he began to bark hoarsely, and
grandfather said, "My dear Irma, I cannot bear this animal out
of doors either!" Aunt Irma quickly rang for her maid and
demanded a glass of sherry. The Pekinese had to be taken
upstairs. Aunt Elsa said nothing but closed her eyes and sighed
meaningfully behind her pink egret feathers.

At night there were lanterns on Aunt Klara's terrace, red
and blue and white, grandfather's favorite colors. The older
generation stayed in the garden which was full of evening
fragrance, and the young people sneaked through the hedge
to the terrace, where champagne corks began to pop. The man
at the piano played and sang "Ramona." Sonia and I sat hidden in the bushes; they had forgotten all about us in the dark,
and we were careful not to attract attention. The sky was
already studded with stars, so many of them; only a very thin
light line remained in the west, but even that disappeared
soon. Only the stars remained and the lanterns, red and blue
and white, and some hesitant fireflies. My father danced with
my mother, holding her as if he never wanted to let her go,
and I was slightly jealous and very happy at the same time.

After the summer the brown house in School Street always waited for us like an old friend. As soon as the taxi
stopped in front of the house, Franziska would dash upstairs
to unlock the door and open the shutters. We had to undergo
the welcoming ceremony of the Misses Paskud. Both ladies
came out of their slightly rancid-smelling doorway. Little Miss
Sidonie held on to my mother's hand and was amazed at how

much I had grown over the summer. Little Miss Anna ran into the apartment and came back with four liqueur glasses. Each time I wondered whether the sliwowitz, which was offered to my parents to celebrate our return, also had that faint rancid smell.

After supper—grandmother's ham rolls, left over from the journey—I absolutely had to go out again to see my friends. There was Ernestine, grubbier than ever, this time with a handkerchief because her summery dress had short sleeves. There was wild Rudi, his knees and elbows scraped almost beyond recognition. He knew how to spit through his teeth like a pro now, and in my absence he had counted all his freckles; there were two hundred and eighty-seven of them, including those nobody could see.

I admired Rudi tremendously: not everybody could spit through his teeth like that, not everybody could count all his freckles. But how did freckles get to places where nobody could see them? I asked my mother about that, and she laughed and said that Rudi was up to no good, and that I would not be allowed to play alone with him in the washhouse anymore. I did not understand what Rudi's freckles had to do with the washhouse, and I was mad at my mother because she did not understand. I loved Rudi and did not want him humiliated.

Water rats lived in the brook, and sometimes when Ernestine and Rudi and I would lie on the bank and keep absolutely still, we would see them moving along the riverbed like long dark shadows. The water ran swiftly, and wherever the sun touched it, the bottom sparkled with the shards of glass that littered the bed. The water rats and the quick stream would not have prevented us from bathing in the brook on hot summer days; it was only the shiny pieces of glass that made us keep a respectful distance. We did not need Franziska's warnings; we knew for ourselves that the mysterious glimmer and glow was not from shards and garbage: these were the treasures of the water sprite, which no mortal was ever allowed to touch.

In the fall my father went hunting, and I could go with him as far as the forester's house. Walking through the meadows and then the forest, I held his hand and listened. He knew many stories about the woods and could show me exactly how to count rings on the tree trunks, and where they would be planting a nursery, and where they would be cutting trees next spring. From time to time I looked up at him: he was wearing a green hunting suit and a green hat with a chamois bristle. His gun was slung over his shoulder, the barrel pointing downward. I was very proud of him. No one in the whole wide world had a father as handsome and clever as mine.

In the forester's garden we drank a glass of buttermilk, and then we parted. My father and the forester went deeper into the woods, where they would spend the night in a hay barn before going to the blind at dawn. I waited until the forester's maid could lead me back through the forest to the edge of town. Old Mr. Alois was just lighting the gas lights on School Street, and it felt good to come back to the protective warmth of the house.

The buck and the hares, sometimes a pheasant, would be brought to the kitchen later, cold and still and covered with pine branches. My mother and Franziska would be kept very busy. In the fall, company came almost every day. My father liked to be among people, he had friends everywhere, and he extended invitations to them, as he did everything, with infectious enthusiasm. It happened quite often that his friends who had come for dinner would still be sitting more or less upright in the dining room when Franziska got up in the morning to light the kitchen fire.

My father had become proficient in Czech since his marriage. When I was little, he still could not distinguish between the masculine and feminine endings of Czech verbs and, probably to amuse me, referred to himself in the feminine form. Later he spoke fluently, even though his accent made my mother laugh and shake her head.

When my parents had first come to the town in eastern Czechoslovakia, my father was looked upon with mistrust for a while. A German who had a Czech wife—and Jewish to boot —who clearly adored her, who spoke Czech with his associates and who liked to be instructed in the intricacies of Czech grammar—wasn't he a strange mixture? Should one not be on guard here, should one not exercise the utmost caution? The man clearly belonged neither to the German camp nor to the Czechs; surely that was reason enough to be suspicious.

As time went by, the people became reconciled to the situation, understanding that my father was not intent on provoking anyone. He was such a pleasant man, a cheerful companion—no spoilsport. And what made them like him best was the fact that he never tried to push his way into either of the groups.

My father was aware of his peculiar position. Sometimes, when he got to talking in Mr. Pavlista's wine cellar, he called himself a man who sat between two stools. "But don't think that I ever feel unhappy about that," he went on to say. "Sitting between your stools I might be able to be a bridge from one to the other."

That was something they liked to hear. The exception was the school principal, who had known from the very beginning on which stool he was going to be sitting and who wore white kneesocks on Czechoslovak patriotic occasions, thus demonstrating his allegiance to the Nazis. He tolerated my father with a mocking smile and acknowledged my mother's existence only very grudgingly.

When I turned six and was supposed to start school, the whole town watched; would I be sent to the German elementary school? But my parents had decided on that question even before I had been born: I would be brought up in the language of my mother. The wearers of the white kneesocks waited in vain for a sign that my father was begging to join their group.

In first grade I discovered my great liking for numbers. The number four especially intrigued me; I covered whole pages in my copybooks with these number fours; the sharp angle and the decisive line through the figure I drew over and over and could not get enough. When election time came in the spring of that year and various political parties were represented by numbers, I was very delighted to find that even grownups had a weakness for numerals. "Vote 1" the posters said, and "Vote 5" was painted on all the sidewalks. Just for me, they also wrote "Vote 4."

Secretly I bought a piece of chalk and set out to decorate the house on School Street according to my preference. I wrote "Vote 4" on all the stairs, on the brown front door, on all the walls as high as I could reach, even on the black and white tiles in the halls. I was very proud of the beautiful angles and lines. But my father did not think them beautiful at all. With Franziska's help I had to hurry to wash off everything I had written, and Franziska even slapped me for it. That year number 4 was the party of the white kneesocks, and my father said, "They're making far too much noise even without your help!" Then he inquired whether anybody had instructed me to decorate the house in that manner. Upset at this further humiliation, I yelled that I did not need anyone to write such beautiful numbers for me, I could certainly do it all by myself!

My parents looked at each other, and all of a sudden they seemed to find the situation very funny. My mother laughed out loud, and my father turned away so that I would not see his laughter. I was furious at both of them and sulked for a whole evening.

Georgie Kitchner, the pale boy who lived next door, was sick for a long time. He did not come outside to play, was not allowed to run, and would stare at us with sad eyes as we sprinted off toward the brook. Once, on a sunny day in late fall, he stepped out of his house with a handful of raspberry candies. He held them in the palm of his hand into the sunshine and smiled. The raspberry candies threw reddish glints onto his hand. Then Rudi came running, he hit Georgie's hand from below, and all the beautiful red raspberry candies flew into the air. Rudi threw himself down to collect them, and Ernestine and I, too, did what we could. Georgie began to cry quietly and went back inside. We ran to the brook with our loot. There we fell into the grass and could not stop laughing at all. We sucked the red candies until the soft filling stuck to our tongues and to our teeth before it melted. Our tongues turned red, and we were so thrilled by that discovery that we started howling all over again.

After that we did not see Georgie for a long time. He did not come outside. His mother always looked at me so sadly when I met her that I never dared to ask after him. I ran away instead.

In early spring he died. A black-bordered announcement with his name on it was put up in the classroom. I stared at it, and suddenly I had a disgusting taste of raspberry candies in my mouth. I mumbled something and ran out of the room to wash out my mouth. But even then the taste would not leave. At lunchtime I threw up.

In the afternoon our whole class went to look at Georgie Kitchner in his coffin. He lay on a white satin pillow, a candle in his hands. This was not the real Georgie Kitchner, but a strange yellow face above Georgie Kitchner's Sunday suit. I ran home as if someone was chasing me, broke open my piggy bank, ran to the candy store, and bought a bagful of red raspberry candies. Clutching them, I hurried back to Georgie Kitchner's coffin. The schoolchildren had left already, an old woman was the only person kneeling there. I sneaked closer and put the bag on the white satin pillow, next to the strange yellow face.

Then I ran out again, I ran to my mother as if someone were after me, I threw myself at her and cried and screamed and tried to scream the taste of raspberries away. My mother hugged me and put me to bed. The next morning I was well, but I could never eat raspberry candies again. And I never played with Rudi again.

At night my parents would often sit by the radio and listen to a voice that threatened and chided and yelped. But no one in the radio audience seemed to mind. On the contrary, they clapped and demanded that the voice go on and on threatening and yelping, again and again, until it turned hoarse and was finally drowned by martial music and wild cries. Then my father would turn the radio off abruptly and look very angry. My mother would sit there darning my stockings. She worked very quickly and with great concentration and did not look up. It was as if she could not forgive the large holes and had to punish them with all the might of her needle.

Then I saw my mother crying for the first time. On a morning in September, my father had finished shaving and turned on the radio. But the radio did not play a trumpet-polka as usual; a halting male voice announced that President Masaryk had died during the night. My father lowered his head and leaned on the table as if all at once his strength had left him. Franziska came running from the kitchen and slowly folded her hands. I went to my mother, wanting to be comforted. But she sat still and did not see me; her eyes were very far away, looking many years ahead, and two tears rolled slowly down my mother's smooth cheeks until, very quietly, they fell into her lap. Later I often saw my mother cry, sadly and angrily and in despair. But never again did I see that endless look in her eyes, the look which showed that she was resigned to her fate.

Black flags dangled from the staffs, and the photograph in our classroom was framed in black. For days people spoke only in whispers. Grandmother wrote that grandfather had suddenly aged and that he had begun talking of selling the business and retiring. Nothing seemed to make him happy any more, grandmother's letter said.

Little Miss Sidonie Paskud taught us knitting and crocheting and embroidery. Between cross-stitches and runaway needles she liked to tell stories about mysterious and spooky happenings, about travelers who had lost their way and were led home by kind lights or led astray by evil ones, about thunderstorms that sent churning fireballs into people's houses. We listened breathlessly and very often forgot all about our stitches and loops.

Sometimes I was permitted to help Miss Paskud with her storytelling, because, she said, I had the wildest imagination. Then I would frighten even myself, goose pimples would run down my spine when I told about the water sprite who sat under the old willow tree in the brook and held drowned souls imprisoned under little mugs, and about Death, who could sneak through doors even when they were tightly locked. Miss Paskud nodded thoughtfully and bent her head with its thinning hair over her knitting; after she had held the needles for a while, they too would have a slightly rancid smell.

None of us would ever have dared to leave the classroom during these lessons. We sat without moving and jumped when clumsy Ernestine dropped her needle. The ringing of the school bell broke the spell, we packed up our workbaskets and cautiously stepped out into the hallway. The boys coming

from the gym made an enormous racket; Rudi tried to trip me
and pulled Olga's pigtails.

Downstairs, near the janitor's apartment, Barry the Saint
Bernard lay on his blanket. He raised his head when he saw
us coming and beat the floor with his tail. Then he slowly rose,
stretched and yawned, and went to stand near the door. Barry
belonged to Antonia, whose father had an inn in the forest,
two hours away, and Barry brought Antonia to school and
home again, every day and in all kinds of weather. During the
day he slept on his blanket, and the janitor fed him his lunch.

Rudi walked behind Miss Paskud making faces. I took
Miss Paskud's hand and squeezed it. Miss Paskud was now
smaller than I, and I wanted to protect her, although I knew
that my hands would have the slightly rancid smell later on.
I hated Rudi.

The blossoms on the chestnut trees quivered in the warm
air. All the windows of the high school were open and, in one
of the classrooms on the third floor, girls' voices were heard
to sing, "Spring is coming, beautiful May . . ."

"I wish I knew," said Ernestine, walking next to me,
"what the world looks like from up there, high up on the third
floor."

Ernestine, I thought, you really are dumb: you've never
been to a third floor in all your life. Even our classroom, which
is on a perfectly ordinary second floor, made you gape for
weeks.

"That's nothing," I said and felt very important. "My
uncle who lives in Prague lives on the fifth floor, and from up
there all the people in the street look just like ants."

Ernestine turned her face to me, grubby and moist above the mouth, and sighed in adoration. An uncle who lived in Prague, and on the fifth floor besides, was as unfathomable to her as the water sprites and the fireballs. A lark was suspended over us in the blue sky, rejoicing. I'll have to show Ernestine everything, I thought, when we grow up. The world is full of mysterious things, and Ernestine is so dumb. She won't understand.

Then came a summer at the grandparents' which was unlike the others. The roses and the phlox were in bloom as always, and grandfather's strawberries tasted as they always had, warm and sweet. The spreading rhubarb leaves provided blissful shade on hot summer afternoons as always. When the wind blew, the green weathervane on the roof of the lawn swing turned this way and that as always. On rainy days the attic smelled of secrets and of sun-warmed wood as always.

But many things were different. Grandfather no longer went to his office. The back garden gate which led to the yards and to the warehouses, and which grandfather had used so rarely because he liked to be seen in the street—it had been walled in. The yards and the warehouses and the office were no longer part of the property: grandfather had sold the business. The letters and the newspapers that were brought to the house by Mr. Maly, the mailman, were addressed not to Max Löwy, Transports, but to Max Löwy, pure and simple.

Aunt Ella had taken off her elbow guards and had moved to Prague. She had distanced herself from the family more than her two sisters had ever dared. Instead of living with the banker uncle, she lived completely alone in an apartment in the New Quarter of Prague. She even dared to write letters filled with enthusiasm about her work with an export firm and about her new independent life. My grandfather, who in the beginning had had a great deal to say on the subject of export firms and young girls who lived in apartments completely alone, was silent; only once in a while he shot a grim look from under his bushy eyebrows.

That summer the villa next door housed not only my friend Sonia and her little brother, but also two cousins from Vienna. Both cousins were nearsighted and slightly older than we, and all they ever wanted to play was civil war. In the morning, in the afternoon, civil war all the time. For a while we played civil war with them, but we soon tired of being constantly beaten up and wounded and even dead, and we returned to the quiet lawn behind the house and to our dolls.

The cousins complained to Aunt Klara, and Aunt Klara slapped Sonia and said something about courtesy and hospitality to be shown to friends in need. We did not quite understand, because the cousins were cousins and not friends, and they were not in need because they had many trunks and were on their way to Australia. They were waiting for their parents and for their visa, and we asked Mr. Maly the mailman every morning if he was bringing it at long last. A visa for the cousins seemed to us to be the guarantee that things would be again as they had been before. Mr. Maly let us look through his mail pouch and said, "We will all be needing a visa soon, children." But that was no real comfort.

The cousins' parents really did come from Vienna for

grandfather's birthday. They brought even more trunks with them, and Aunt Klara had the baby nurse moved to Sonia's room. Sonia grew fiercely angry, she did not want to have the baby nurse in her room, and Aunt Klara said, "You are really spoiled rotten." The cousins giggled with malice; they did not have their own rooms any more either.

Over her afternoon coffee Aunt Marta, the cousins' mother, talked in a quiet voice for a long time. The others sat in silence and stared into their coffee cups. Even Aunt Elsa stopped fanning herself and sat still. Then one of the cousins called out, "And what is Hitler doing, Mama? Is he still crazy?" Sonia and I began to laugh; it was the first funny thing we had heard from the cousins all summer.

But Aunt Marta did not think it funny at all, she jumped up and whispered, "Will you be quiet? You'll make trouble for all of us here!" She looked all around anxiously, as if she were scared of us and even of the trees.

The visa finally arrived toward the end of the summer. Mr. Maly waved the letter all the way up the sidewalk, and the cousins and their parents were leaving. We took them to the railroad station, and we kissed them, happy that we would not have to play civil war any more.

Aunt Marta cried when she hugged my grandfather and said, "Please be careful, all of you." And grandfather patted her shoulder and said, "Nothing will happen to us here, don't you worry. We belong here."

The train began to move, and for a long time we could see the four handkerchiefs like whirling white dots moving with the train. Then they disappeared, but the tracks con-

tinued their humming for a while longer. Sonia got her room
back, and we did not play civil war any more. But nothing was
the same again.

The following summer I turned eleven. Before Franziska
and I left to go to the grandparents', my mother took me aside
and showed me the summer clothes she had bought for me:
all the bathing suits had tops. There was a pair of shorts with
a matching halter which one was supposed to tie on the neck.
There were white polo shirts which I was expected to wear to
cover my chest. I was appalled at these new inventions.

That night I spent a long time examining myself in the
mirror. I was very thorough, but there was nothing special to
be seen. Only sometimes, when I felt cold and my arms had
goose pimples I would feel tickling, running almost all the way
up to my shoulders and under my armpits, until it reached my
nipples and came to rest there for a while.

My grandmother shook her head when she saw my new
outfits. But since she did not say anything about them, I remained silent also and wore them with my teeth clenched, as
if they were a mark of shame. Only when Sonia turned out to
be madly envious of the halter was I finally reconciled to my
new situation. And when I saw that my elegant Aunt Klara
sometimes wore the same kind of halter with her white trousers, I even began to feel sorry for poor Sonia, who was two
years younger and was not yet one of us, the ladies.

Sonia's little brother joined us that summer, and we
would put up with him as we sat on the blanket in the sunny
grass behind the house. We made him babysit our dolls and

wash all the doll dishes. We also let him help us in the park across the road where, in a dark hidden hedge near the fence, we had built a small cemetery. We searched the neighborhood for dead sparrows and beetles, and every tiny corpse we found we buried with much pomp and ceremony. After packing it into a cardboard box, we would wheel it three times around the park in a doll carriage before, moaning and weeping copiously, we laid it to rest. We decorated the small grave with grandfather's most beautiful begonias and carnations, and we made crosses from Emma's kindling wood. The gravestones bore melancholy inscriptions, written in ink and profusely decorated with curlicues.

The area near the park fence was dark; the smell of rotting blossoms, of dead leaves, of moist earth was everywhere, and we knew that the souls of the dead were pleased with our actions. When matters became too threatening and we became frightened of each other, we would run back to Sonia's garden, where the swimming pool twinkled in the sunshine and where the baby nurse had our snacks ready under the polka-dotted umbrella: slices of bananas and oranges laced with raspberry syrup. The bananas had a sweet scent, and the red umbrella and the red raspberry syrup lent them a pink hue.

Sonia's little brother was a fussy eater. He would still be sitting over his dish when Sonia and I had long since finished our portions, and he would drip big tears onto his banana slices. Not until the baby nurse took our plates back to the house—in order, as she said, not to make a banquet for the flies—could we reach for the little boy's portion and relieve him of his suffering.

Aunt Klara did not spend much time in the garden that summer. She had acquired something which grandfather, with a frown, called "the new toy." It was not a toy at all, but a small red car with two seats and spoke wheels and without any roof at all. It made a lot of noise when Aunt Klara drove it out of the garage and around the corner. Even after it had disappeared behind the park hedges, and when we could no longer see Aunt Klara's white scarf fluttering in the breeze, we could still hear the humming of the motor. The humming also announced Aunt Klara's return, then the white scarf above the shiny red metal appeared among the trees, and then Aunt Klara's happy face loomed up behind the low windshield.

Once Aunt Klara took all three of us for a drive. Sonia and I crouched on the seat and clung to each other as best we could, and little John held onto the tiny luggage space behind the seats. The speed of Aunt Klara's driving took our breath away, her white scarf looked ready to fly off at any moment. This was not grandfather's comfortable Škoda with old Wenzel at the wheel; it was something entirely different. I adored my beautiful, dashing Aunt Klara and determined to be just like her when I grew up.

But when I came home out of breath and reported on our outing, grandfather grew angry. His bushy eyebrows twisted even more fiercely than usual, and he sent Franziska to bring Aunt Klara over.

When she arrived, she was still wearing her white driving gloves. She sat in the drawing room with her legs crossed and laughed when grandfather, using his loudest voice, forbade her to take any of us driving ever again. "You will break your neck one day," grandfather said, and his forehead purpled. I sat cuddled up in a rocking chair and mourned Aunt Klara, who would break her neck one day. But Aunt Klara did not seem at all distraught. The little red car whizzed around the park hedges with its usual humming the very next morning, and the white scarf went on fluttering cheerfully.

That summer was Franziska's last at the grandparents' house. She was getting married in the fall. But the groom was not the handsome trumpet player in the military band who had enchanted her in the music pavilion some years ago. She was going to marry Aunt Klara's factory driver, who owned a small house on the outskirts of town and who came to help out with the gardening some evenings. Franziska would watch him from the hedge; he had black eyes and was tall and thin, with many muscles, and Franziska was up to her ears in love with him. I was a bit disappointed about this development; I had liked the trumpet player much better. But Franziska said that I did not understand about those things and that I should just keep nice and quiet.

She spent whole days in the sewing room next to the attic working on her trousseau. Grandmother had given her a bolt of linen and had told her to do with it as she pleased. The sewing machine rattled from morning to night, and when Franziska came downstairs for her meals, she had pinpricks on her fingertips and linen threads on her skirt. But at night, when the factory driver took off his shirt to mow the lawn, she stood at the hedge and laughed a lot, and her ears were bright red.

Before grandfather's birthday she finally abandoned the

sewing room to help with the baking. "What an honor to see you in the kitchen," Emma said and pushed a bowl of egg yolks toward Franziska. "Beat those." The two kitchen maids poked one another and giggled.

Then for a time everything was as it had always been. The house was fragrant with vanilla and nuts, Emma stood in the kitchen and gave orders that had to be obeyed, and the pantry shelves filled up. We had many parties on the sunny lawn behind the house, and even little John, who did not like banana salad, ate a lot of burned cake crumbs and leftover lemon icing.

The three aunts from Aussig arrived in a taxi that year, because grandfather's Škoda had been sold with the business and old Wenzel had retired. I noticed for the first time that the hair of all three aunts was almost white. Johanna, the oldest, walked with a stoop, and Regina and Theresa, the youngest of Grandfather's sisters, no longer laughed and did not joke as they used to; they embraced grandmother quietly. And grandmother's face remained as serious as her eyes had always been. At coffee time the spoons and cups tinkled on the veranda as always. But the laughter was missing. Aunt Johanna's hands shook as she patted my head, and later, during her yearly stroll through the garden, she leaned heavily on grandfather, as if she would never be able to walk upright again.

The banker uncle from Prague came alone that summer. His wife, Aunt Olga, suffered from a heavy mind, he said, and did not want to travel. I did not know what suffering from a heavy mind meant; when I asked old Emma in the kitchen, she said, "Go and play with Sonia, little Helenka," and she quickly gave me a piece of poppyseed cake. We pretended that all our dolls suffered from heavy minds. But after a while the game palled, because we did not know the proper cure for heavy minds—compresses or camomile tea—and we sent little John to get us more poppyseed cake.

Only the Warnsdorfers arrived with their usual pomp. The two Humbers were shinier than ever; glass and chrome reflected the onlookers, the two chauffeurs were dressed in pale blue with silver buttons, and Aunt Elsa's fan took up the entire back seat. The Pekinese in the other car had a pale blue ribbon to match, and he yelped angrily at everybody who approached.

Grandfather did not come out of the house to greet his two brothers; he waited for them in the hall. After he had kissed them both and kissed the ladies' hands, he said, "You shouldn't show off like this in these times—maybe a little modesty would be more fitting." But Uncle Fritz laughed and drank his glass of sherry in one gulp, and Uncle Rudolf put his arm around grandfather's shoulder and said, "Nobly shall we perish, my dear Max!"

That night Aunt Irma was indisposed. She and the Pekinese remained upstairs alone, and the chambermaid brought them ice packs. In the kitchen I waited for old Emma to sit down on her window seat for a rest, and then I asked, "Aunt Irma, is she suffering from a heavy mind too?" But old Emma shook her head and said, "Not her, little Helenka, not that one. And who knows, maybe she's better off."

On the morning of grandfather's birthday I was playing outside, under the drawing-room window. The carnation beds

there were bordered with bricks, which I was decorating with
pebbles from the path. In the drawing room above me I heard
voices. The banker uncle was there, grandfather, Aunt Klara's
father, and the two uncles from Warnsdorf—all the five brothers. Blue mist wafted through the window. "They really do
smoke like factory chimneys," I said to myself and giggled,
and then I climbed the apricot tree to listen.

"I've already sold all the inland stocks," said Uncle Fritz,
"and have traded them in for good Swiss ones."

"To hell with the factories," said Uncle Rudolf, and his
voice sounded almost cheerful, as it had sounded when he had
said, "Nobly shall we perish." "The ones in Bucarest," he
continued, "maybe we can still save those, but Warnsdorf is
as good as lost."

"I find it simply irresponsible," said grandfather's voice,
and it sounded angry; surely grandfather's forehead would be
red and the vein in the middle of it visible. "If everybody did
what the two of you are doing, the market would crash in a
week, and that's exactly what Hitler is waiting for! Where is
your solidarity? Aren't you patriots?"

"Solidarity?" said Uncle Fritz, and I imagined how he
moved his large head while speaking. "Patriotism? We all
should leave, Max, with kith and kin, while we still can!"

"Leave here? Where for?" That was the banker uncle's
voice. It sounded sad and hoarse. Did he, too, suffer from a
heavy mind?

"To France, to England, to America, what do I know,"
said Uncle Fritz. "Away from here, while we've still got the
chance."

"But we belong here," said Aunt Klara's father. "We were born here, our father is buried here, our grandfather is buried here. Where are we supposed to run to, damn it all?"

They were silent for a long time.

"As long as I am head of the family," my grandfather said, and he must have walked over to the window, because his voice sounded louder and more threatening than usual. "As long as I live, not one of us will run away, do you understand? This country will need each one of us, very soon, and we will all be here when it needs us. I will not tolerate any talk about emigration in my house. None. Do you understand?"

The drawing room became so still that I could clearly hear Uncle Fritz pulling on his pipe. Then someone pushed aside an ashtray, and Aunt Klara's father coughed twice. The blue mist moved out of the window and flew away.

My left leg had gone to sleep on the branch of the apricot tree and began to ache. I jumped down, suppressing a whimper. As I stomped along the pebbled path, little stones pushed their way into my sandals and hurt; I bent down, picked up a handful of them, and threw them against the fir trees. Then I began to cry.

Aunt Ella stayed on after all the other guests had left. She was an entirely new Aunt Ella. She wore narrow linen dresses with large buttons and small hats that revealed her forehead and covered the nape of her neck. She always wore one of her hats when she took me to the pastry shop in the afternoons, and people would nod to her and say, "Look at little Ella, she's a young lady now!"

I tried to keep step with Aunt Ella and to eat pineapple

tarts the way she did, but my legs were too short and my fingers too clumsy, and Aunt Ella laughed at me. Her black eyes were shining, and she had the darkest eyebrows I had ever seen: they were as thick as grandfather's, except that his were bushy and wild, while hers were as soft as velvet. My greatest wish was to have long eyelashes and soft eyebrows like Aunt Ella, but when I told her, she laughed and said, "Don't wish that. Then you would have all kinds of shaving problems, like me. But don't breathe a word to grandfather."

Aunt Ella spent many hours sitting with grandmother in the wicker chairs on the veranda. They whispered a lot, and if I dared to come too near, they always made some excuse to send me away. Once Aunt Ella wept, she blew her nose several times, and put her head in grandmother's lap. Grandmother stroked her hair. Her hands looked like fragile white flowers in Aunt Ella's black curls.

Soon after, I heard grandfather's voice in the drawing room. It was his angriest voice, his forehead surely must have been red as he said, "You are not going to marry a Jew! We have enough Jews in the family, and I am tired of them all! And he wants to go to America, Mr. Smarty, of all places!" Then newspapers rustled to announce that grandfather had spoken, and after a while he added, somewhat more pleasantly, "Besides, he is much too old for you. You are just twenty-three, he could almost be your father." The newspapers rustled again, grandfather cleared his throat, and all was quiet.

I went to hide in the kitchen and was very angry. It seemed to me that never before that summer had all the grown-ups had so many secrets. The kitchen was empty, Emma's window seat was deserted. The kitchen clock ticked and wheezed softly. I sat down on the worn black leather seat and felt very lonely.

My mother found me there and sat down with me, and then I began to cry and to say angry things. My mother stroked my head just as grandmother had done for Aunt Ella, and her eyes had a dreamy look. "Aunt Ella wants to marry her boss in Prague, and grandfather does not like him," she explained. She looked out the window, where grandfather's rose trees were waiting for the breeze, and she smiled at something that seemed far away. "She loves him and he must love her, too. Otherwise he would have left for America without her a long time ago."

I had stopped crying and was nodding with deep understanding. My heart was beating wildly because my mother was discussing matters of such importance with me. Suddenly I was very proud of myself: I knew about secrets and understood about them, and I could wear a halter over my chest. I was grown up.

Then it came time to say good-bye to Franziska, and Franziska bawled so much that her nose turned red and she did not want to let go of me at all, until my mother said, "You better stop right now, or I'll start crying myself." The factory driver patted Franziska's back, and she finally stopped bawling, but her nose was still red when we drove to the railroad station.

The train trip that year took much longer than usual, the train was stopped on the tracks for hours while one freight train after another passed at full speed. The railroad stations were filled with soldiers in green uniforms, all waiting to go someplace.

At home the little Misses Paskud were waiting for us as usual. Miss Sidonie said, "My goodness, how the child has grown!" and Miss Anna poured four glasses of sliwowitz. They had had their apartment painted during the summer, it did not smell as rancid as before, but the two ladies still made worried faces and said, "God only knows what will happen to all of us!"

The following day I sat by the brook with grubby Ernestine, who wept fat tears and wiped them off with her skirt because both her sleeves were already soaked through. Her father, a train conductor, had been called into military service that very morning, and Ernestine, her eyes big as saucers, said, "It's mobilization, you know." I comforted her as well as I could by telling her, "The most important thing is that he has his health," as I had heard my mother say so often. I had no idea what "mobilization" meant, but I could not confess my ignorance to Ernestine.

Wild Rudi ran past us, carrying a branch to which he had attached a frayed piece of rope. He was playing war. When he saw us, he stopped to remark, "Listen, Ernestine, you better not talk to that kid here, her father is a German!"

Never before had I thought that the term could be an insult, but Rudi's tone of voice told me that it was one now. I jumped up and threw myself at Rudi; I had grown taller than he and all my hatred came pouring out now, the raspberry candies and Georgie Kitchner. I pummeled and scratched and bit, and Rudi tried to defend himself, but finally he abandoned his gun and ran away. Ernestine shouted bad words at his departing back.

I limped home, my hands bleeding, my back aching where Rudi's branch gun had hit me, and my cheek swelling to cover my eye. My mother said, "For heaven's sake, child," and began to wash me. She questioned and inquired and tried to find out what happened, but I would not tell and I did not cry. When my father came home, he asked no questions. Hugging me, he said, "Don't forget, Helenka, whatever happens now, we have to stick together."

Then came days when my parents did nothing but sit by the radio. The screaming, bellowing voice was often heard, and lots of military bands, and then only time signals for hours and hours. Once a halting voice listed names of border towns that had been given up to Hitler without a single shot, and my mother crossed them off on a map and shook her head and said, "But we cannot exist without them."

Mrs. Bejlek, who owned the tobacconist's shop across the street, came running upstairs. She was also holding a map, and she said to my father, "All they left us is a little sausage, your honor, nothing but a little sausage!" Then she stayed in the dining room, irresolute, refusing to sit down, simply weeping into a black-bordered handkerchief.

When school finally began again, the photograph of the new president had been installed above the blackboard. Nobody knew anything about him; he looked old and tired, and our teacher made a speech to tell us that this was the man who would be taking care of our country, which had been deserted by everyone.

The principal began to wear his white kneesocks even on ordinary days, and he no longer spoke to my mother. My father received letters from his family in the Sudetenland, many letters each week all of a sudden. He either did not read them at all or he tore them up angrily. The new wrinkle that had formed between his eyebrows during the summer did not disappear.

That fall he did not go hunting. My mother put mothballs into the pockets of the green suit and stored it away with the summer clothes. When my father's friends came to visit now, they were not happy and noisy as they had been. Most often they sat by the radio and spoke in excited whispers. "They are talking politics," my mother said. They no longer stayed until morning.

Aunt Ella's wedding took place that fall in Prague. Grandfather had finally given his consent. In the wedding photographs her husband, Uncle Fred, looked nice, tall and thin, with glasses and a secret smile. Aunt Ella wore a gray flannel suit trimmed with fur and one of her tiny hats. She seemed even more elegant and more worthy of imitation than Aunt Klara. "Will they go to America soon now?" I asked my mother breathlessly. America was far away, so far that no one who went there ever came back.

"No, they won't," said my mother. She shook her head and sighed. "Uncle Fred's visa is invalid now. And he probably won't get another, because there is something wrong with his lungs. But grandfather must not know about that."

I breathed a sigh of relief. Aunt Ella would not be leaving; she would stay and be here for me.

For Christmas that year I was given a pair of skis, and after my first grim attempts I had mastered the art of skiing. I lost all interest in any other activity. As soon as I came home from school I would begin to change; first I put on the thick stockings, then the sheepswool socks, then the navy wool ski pants, and finally my pride and joy, the beautiful ski boots, shiny, with two fancy buckles each. Proudly I marched over the bridge, across the bleaching meadow, all the way to the firs, where a gentle hill rose behind the little chapel. One part of the slope had been smoothed by sleds: in spots the grass showed through, but right below the chapel there was a beautiful patch of powder where I could practice my stem christies and my telemarks for as long as I wanted.

Sometimes grubby Ernestine came along. She would sit on her sled and watch me with admiration until dusk began to fall on the hill and the light in the chapel shone like a red fire in the darkness. Only then did I undo my bindings and load the skis on Ernestine's sled. Ernestine sighed and pulled, and we stomped off toward town. On the way we made several angels: we lay flat on our backs and carefully moved our arms and legs until the imprint on the snow looked like a figure with wings and a long skirt. It was a real art to get up in such a way that the angel figure was not smudged. Then we continued toward home, two little dots in the endless white meadow.

Then March came and the days grew longer, snow-drops once more raised their pale bells in the garden, and the snow was no longer powdery. It quickly turned soft and gray on the sunny slopes. One last time I came down the hill like an expert, and the light in the chapel formed a small reddish arch in the snow above me.

Ernestine waited patiently beside her sled, and I sat down to undo my bindings. Then both of us stiffened: something unusual was in the air. We looked at each other, and for a while we did not quite know what was the matter. Then we nodded in unison; we agreed on what we had heard. The bells had been sounding for a while already from the church tower. But it was not a single bell that rang across the white meadow —all the bells in the tower were tolling, the four small ones along with the largest one that was rung only on Sundays. Now all were clanging as if they never intended to stop.

"Something horrible must have happened," I said and grabbed Ernestine's sleeve. Abandoning the sled and the skis in the snow, we started to run.

Never before did the way home seem so long. We panted and fell down, the wet snow sticking to our feet. My hands were freezing because I had left my mittens alongside the skis. And the bells: no longer sounding a death toll, they clanged and clattered as if to burst the church tower.

The gas lamps had not yet been lit, although it was already dark. "Maybe Mr. Alois died?" Ernestine wondered. No, no one would ring all the bells for Mr. Alois; one would be enough. It had to be something much worse.

We ran through School Street. No one was in sight. Far below, where narrow School Street led into the highway, there were lights, and the lights were moving. A low roar rose

—the roar of many engines. The people standing down below were silent as the engines passed noisily. No one said a word. It took us a long time to push our way through the crowd. The bells went on and on.

And then we saw the soldiers, on motorcycles, on trucks, on tanks. But they did not wear the well-known green uniforms, and they did not smile at us, and they did not wave at us as soldiers usually did. They were all in gray, an endless column of gray soldiers with gray helmets, all looking straight ahead as if they still had a long way to go. Only the men standing on trucks holding machine guns—they looked at us. But they did not smile; their guns were pointed at us.

There was no school the next day, and I went back to the meadow to pick up my skis and my mittens and Ernestine's sled. The bells had fallen silent. During the night the snow had begun to melt in earnest. Small rivulets flowed downhill, and the round roof of the chapel was dripping. Skiing was finished for the season. And the soldiers, my mother said, were now in Prague.

That evening we had a telephone call from Prague. My father, clutching the receiver, was made to wait a long time; the connection was bad, strange voices kept breaking in. For a long time he could not even make out who was calling. It was Rose, the banker uncle's old housekeeper. She was weeping and could not talk very coherently. The banker uncle and Aunt Olga, his wife, had jumped out of the window that morning as the German soldiers were marching in. Yes, they were both dead. Their apartment was on the fifth floor. Then the censor interrupted the conversation.

Since Franziska was no longer with us, I was allowed to travel alone to visit my grandparents the following summer. My father took me as far as Ostrau and put me on the express train. He hung my coat near the window seat, lifted my suitcase onto the rack, and set the basket holding ham rolls, apricots, and paper napkins next to me. Then he tipped the conductor. Before he left, he gave me a present: a little red leather notebook with a golden pencil. I should, my father said, put down all the names of all the stations the train went past.

This I did faithfully the whole long day. I put down the Czech names and added the German ones—names that I had never heard before that now appeared ahead of the others everywhere. But the ham rolls in the lunch basket remained untouched. At noon, when the dining-car waiter went through the train with his gong, I followed him as I had always done with Franziska. And I liked the meal they served in the dining-car so much that I stayed for the second sitting. Franziska's husband, who came to meet me in Königgrätz, had to settle my dining-car debts. He was still laughing when he deposited me at my grandparents' house. I was deeply offended; could it be that he did not consider me almost grown up?

For the first time since it had been built the old house had a roomer. Mr. Karasek worked at the post office. He was young and his face sported many pimples, and once I heard old Emma complain that the pimples and the creams he used were ruining her bed linens.

Mr. Karasek left early in the morning and returned late at night; he never spoke to anybody in the house. I turned my eyes away: he was an intruder, even though grandmother explained patiently again and again that it was not Mr. Karasek's fault that he had to live with us in the old house.

"He was billeted here, you see," she would say.

"But whose fault is it then, grandmother?" I asked, feeling angry.

She sighed and patted my cheek, and I knew exactly what she wanted to tell me—"Times are very bad, child, you don't understand that yet"—and I tore away, jumped down the three steps of the veranda, and was gone before she could speak.

Grandmother's eyes followed me. They were sadder than they had ever been before, rimmed with dark shadows. Grandfather, too, had aged. His back, which had always been straight, was bent now. His cane had become more than an ornament; when he went for his afternoon walk, he leaned on it heavily. He let old Emma pick all his strawberries now. At the beginning of the summer he stood beside her and told her which ones were to be picked and which ones must be allowed to ripen another day. But as the days passed he no longer came outside, leaving the decisions up to her.

In the hall, the photograph of the old president was missing. The nail remained, as if to hold the pale square visible on the wall. The weathervane on the roof of the garden swing was the only thing that seemed unaware of change, turning merrily as the wind shifted. The swing squeaked now because there was no one to oil it since old Wenzel had retired.

The rear wall of the house had been painted over. It was no longer black, and the white inscription *Max Löwy, Coal and Transport* and the two crossed hammers could no longer be seen. The wall was now yellowish brown to match the rest of the old house.

The swimming pool in Sonia's garden was covered with a grate. Lonely leaves, left from the fall, rustled along its bottom. Sonia and little John spent a lot of time at the old house. The baby nurse had left because she did not want to take care of Jew children. Sonia had repeated the nurse's words and had shrugged her shoulders the way the baby nurse used to do.

Aunt Klara did not go out much. Her little red car stood in the garage, no longer turning corners with a great hum. The white scarf had stopped fluttering. Aunt Klara's eyes were restless, and sometimes she hugged Sonia and little John so hard they almost cried. I avoided Aunt Klara, her eyes frightened me.

Then there was a day that began like any other. Dew dappled the leaves of the strawberry plants, and the balsam firs nodded by the garden gate. We had spread our blanket on the sunny lawn behind the house and built a sunshade from rhubarb leaves. We judiciously berated little John, who was late; as the designated kitchen maid, it was his duty to wash the dolls' breakfast dishes.

A car stopped at Sonia's house. It was a gray military car full of gray soldiers. We left our dolls and tiptoed to the hedge. The soldiers who jumped out all had revolvers strapped to their belts, and they had silver skulls above the visors of their caps. Two of them took up a position at the garden gate, two stood below the steps, and two stepped up to Sonia's front door. Then a second car arrived, it was big and shiny and black; a soldier jumped out and opened the rear door. I was suddenly reminded of the Warnsdorf cars: they too had been big and shiny—but no, this one was different. The man who stepped out of the car was also in gray, but a lot of silver glittered on his shoulders and on his cap under the skull. Hooking his thumbs on his belt, he stood still, his legs in riding boots spread wide, examining Sonia's house as if it were his. Then he slowly took off his gloves. Slowly and deliberately he pulled off one gray glove and then the other. He tapped the gloves against his palm while he walked up the steps to the front door. The soldiers clicked their heels, and the man rang the bell. The door opened and then closed behind him.

One of the soldiers lit a cigarette. Sonia and I, barely breathing, stood at the hedge. A ladybug came to rest in Sonia's hair, but she did not notice. The soldier at the wheel of the first car leaned back and pushed his cap up his forehead. He began to whistle.

A shot rang out inside the house, and then another.

The soldiers raced toward the front door, their revolvers suddenly in their hands. They broke down the front door. The soldier who had sat and whistled jumped over the car door, tearing the revolver from his belt as he ran. And in the house someone screamed, a man's voice was screaming.

Then another shot was fired, and one more, and grandmother came running toward us, her cheeks bright red, and she threw herself at us near the hedge and tried to turn our heads away, but she was not able to—how could she have?— and we saw the soldiers carrying the man with the riding boots out of Sonia's house and into the car, and one of the soldier's hands was all bloody. They put him into the car, his legs in the riding boots were much too long, they had to fold them in, and he was still. Then they drove off, both cars swerved as they turned the park corner, they drove so fast. We heard the tires screeching, and then they were gone.

The front door stayed open and the garden gate also, and then little John came out. He did not have his shoes on yet, he came toward the hedge with tiny steps, his face all white, and he said, "Mommy shot the man, and now she is dead too."

Later many cars came, bringing many soldiers. They carried a stretcher out of Sonia's house and took it away. And in the afternoon they picked up Sonia's father at his factory, and that night they came and picked up Sonia and little John. Then they placed seals on Sonia's front door and on the garage that housed the little red car. "Confiscated for the German Reich," the seals read. The dolls were left in the grass all night, and the breakfast dishes remained unwashed, and I have never seen Sonia and little John again.

I did not want to play outside any more. I sat on the highest plush-covered step, next to the ferns, and stared through the window at Sonia's house for hours. Nothing moved. All the large windows, which had always been bright into the small hours, were dark now. The grass behind the house began to grow tall. Whenever people walked past Sonia's house, they either looked straight ahead or stared at the other side, toward the park. When old Emma went marketing in the morning, she avoided Sonia's house altogether, making a detour to the right to get to the market. She always returned the same way. No one ever talked about what had happened, except for the time when I heard grandfather say, "She is at peace now, but she brought sorrow to her family. And what good did it do?" Grandfather's question remained unanswered. Perhaps he had only been speaking to himself.

Then old Emma took pity and unlocked the attic for me. I could play there even if it didn't rain. The light blue squares of the skylights watched over me, and the world's noise was muted by the time it reached me. Everything was far away. I forgot about Aunt Klara and everything that had happened. I would not play with dolls any more. The dry roof beams creaked now and then as I sat in the rickety wicker rocking chair, reading.

I read whatever I could find in the retired bookcases—Jules Verne, Karl May, Olga Tscharska—and after I had read them all I would borrow Westerns from one of the kitchen maids; she had a stack of them in her room. They were unbound and worn from many a kitchen maid's hands, but I did not mind. Before the summer was over, I knew all there was to know about the Wild West, the prairies and the Rockies had become my home, and Wild Bill Hickok had won my heart. The brown rocking horse with the black mane and the yellow eyes carried me faithfully for days at a time, and as I rode I sang softly, "Oh give me a home, where the buffalo roam . . ." When my parents arrived, I greeted them by raising my left hand, and instead of hugging them, I only said, "How." On that particular day I was an Indian princess, and my name was White Cloud.

Grandmother took my mother aside to remark, "It will

pass, just give her time. It was terrible for all of us."

Then Aunt Zdena, my mother's sister, died in Prague. Her death was very sudden, the result of pneumonia. Grandmother wept loudly in the hall, and her weeping resounded from the marble floor. Everyone said, "Maybe it was a blessing. Who knows what is going to happen to us all?"

Grandfather's birthday was celebrated very quietly. That year, not all the people from Warnsdorf (they lived in Prague now) came. Uncle Rudolf and Uncle Fritz were the only ones to come, and they both came by train. Aunt Johanna, who was also living in Prague now, did not feel strong enough to travel. The two aunts from Aussig had also moved to Prague, and they did not have the slightest trace of laughter in their faces. Aunt Theresa, the younger one, had become even more white-haired since last summer. Coffee was served in the dining room although it was a beautiful day. All avoided going into the garden and looking at Aunt Klara's house. Nobody mentioned it or her.

At night all the curtains were drawn and all the windows were closed before any lights were turned on, as if the old house were a fortress ringed by the enemy, and as if it were a matter of life and death to keep secret from all eyes what went on inside.

The well-wishers from town did not appear until after dark in that year, and even then they turned carefully at the garden gate and looked over their shoulders before slipping inside. Grandfather's eyebrows twitched as he shook the visitors' hands, and he said, "You should not have come, you could get into trouble. You never know who may see you!"

They sat in the drawing room, drank a glass of wine, and said, "Well, what can one do?" Then they took their leave, with great ceremony. They did not make jokes, and even Mr. Councilor, a bachelor, who had always laughed about his embarrassment in the presence of ladies, even he was hushed.

When the two gentlemen from the singing group departed, I tiptoed out after them to see whether they would look to their left and to their right again. They did. They stood still in the shadow of the silver firs, listening to the sound of footsteps somewhere toward town. One of them, Mr. Stoklas, the tenor, shook his head and said, "You don't know what to say to old Löwy any more. How can you wish him many happy years with his family? He doesn't even know what's going to happen to them tomorrow."

The second visitor, Mr. Jenewein, cleared his throat. "They can't even go to the park any more," he said.

Mr. Stoklas said, "Many happy years, damn it all!" and he spat. Then they started walking; the steps that had sounded nearer to town had gone. All was clear.

I had not known that my grandfather could not go to the park. I had not noticed because I had spent the summer reading in the attic. My grandfather had founded the park. Why was he barred from it now?

The following morning I went to the park gate to check whether the park rules made any mention of my grandfather. The rules were there as always, framed in green: we, the public, were not permitted to pick flowers and were requested to keep peace and order. But a new piece of paper was attached to the green frame, tentatively, as if it did not quite belong. It read, "No Jews permitted to enter."

Slowly I went back to the old house. Now I no longer wanted to go to the park. In the kitchen, my mother and grandmother were canning. A row of bottles filled with friendly round peach halves was waiting its turn at the big pot. Old Emma sat on the window seat peeling fruit. Her legs did not seem to want to serve her properly that summer, and she sat down quite often. I hugged and kissed my mother. Her hands and her apron and her face smelled of peaches. She bent down, kissed me back, and laughed. She understood that I had stopped being Buffalo Bill and Princess White Cloud: I was her Helenka. Grandmother stroked my head with her peach-fragrant hands and smiled though her eyes were serious. I said, "Who wants to go to that stupid park, anyway. Not us!"

On the morning of our departure my mother took my hand as we walked through the old house together. We began in the cellar that housed the shiny mountains of coal and the pyramids of firewood, before we visited the smaller cellar with shelves full of grandmother's preserves and grandfather's red wine. Our steps echoed loud and lonely in the hall because we were already wearing our traveling shoes. We opened each door and went inside every room, except for Mr. Karasek's bedroom. It did not belong to the house really.

My mother touched the great-grandparents' heavy double bed, and she touched the blue-flowered bowl and the soap-pot in the dry sink that had been great-grandfather's.

Next we climbed the iron steps to the third floor, where my mother peeked into each of the maids' rooms. Finally we opened the small iron door leading to the attic. We sat for a while on one of the trousseau chests underneath the slanting wall, breathing the hot-dry attic air spiced with the fragrance of wood. My mother did not speak. Much later I understood: she had been saying good-bye to the house of her family.

Then there was war. All the papers wrote about it, but this time the headlines did not say Barcelona and Madrid, but Warsaw and Amsterdam and Brussels. Some nights the window panes rattled when military columns drove down the broad road to the east.

That winter my father received a fat letter from the District Office in the capital. He must appear in person, and the honorable District Officer himself informed him that he must choose between divorcing his wife or immediate retirement. The District Office could no longer tolerate employees who were related to Jews.

My father thanked the District Officer. He picked up his pipe in his office, and he never went there again. His weeping secretary later brought him his law books, his office towel, and a farewell letter from his colleagues.

My father spent days sitting alone at the dining-room table playing chess; from morning 'til night he played one single game. He would leave the black and white figures in place overnight and continued playing the following morning. The game seemed to be without end. When my father finally finished it, I noticed that a new wrinkle had grown above his eyebrows. Several weeks later he went to Prague to look for a new job; his pension was not enough for us to live on. When he came back, my mother told me that we would all be moving to Prague soon.

I cried and did not want to move to Prague. The city was much too big, there was no brook there and no bleaching meadow, and what would grubby Ernestine do without me? Who would show her the world, who would give her orders, whom would she obey? My mother patted my head. "I know, it is very difficult," she said. "But maybe Ernestine could come and visit you one day? Her father works for the railroad, it won't cost her anything to come. Imagine all the things you could show her in Prague!"

That sounded all right. Slowly I got used to the idea and even began to look forward to living in a big city.

Aunt Ella had taken over the job of finding an apartment for us. Soon she had a prospect in a new suburban high-rise: three rooms and a kitchen. The building had just been completed. There were gardens in front and a meadow in back, and the Number Four streetcar went right past. The factory where my father had found a job as legal counsel was not too far away.

When my parents returned from Prague, they seemed pleased. They had liked what Aunt Ella had found for us. Then my mother ordered boxes and started packing. The apartment in School Street began to look inhospitable. Ernestine crouched in her seat and sobbed, and tears rolled slowly down the scratched green surface of her school bench.

We moved in February. The Misses Paskud stood weeping in the hallway, their noses reddened by emotion. They made me a parting gift of a yellow straw hat trimmed with shiny red cherries. As we left the small town in eastern Moravia, the stationmaster raised his signal and waved with his other hand. My father's blue eyes looked back for a long time. Each telegraph pole startled them. Then he straightened up, patted my mother's hand, and said, "There, that part of our lives is behind us."

The new apartment was on the third floor in a row of brand-new apartment houses. Because the tenants had been in a hurry to move in, the building had not even been left to settle over the winter. Everyone tried to get as comfortable as possible as quickly as possible. Times were too uncertain, my mother said, and a damp spot on the wall did not mean much nowadays. Workmen were still going in and out, a door stuck, the bathroom window would not close properly, the railings were not yet installed, the elevator had not been put in. Behind the houses where, according to the janitor, a lawn would grow one day, there were big piles of debris.

Every night I wept secretly in my bed because I missed my nice room in School Street. My new room had no curtains as yet, and my own belongings looked strange in the alien room. The rattling of the Number Four streetcar gave me nightmares. The crunch of sand underfoot, which persisted no matter how much we swept, hurt my ears. Though I was desperately unhappy, I could not say a word to my parents. The three of us had to stick together, my father had said; to complain now would have been betrayal. I pulled my blanket over my head and let my tears soak my pillow.

I carried my unhappiness with me like an unmentionable secret, but my mother must have noticed something. One day she said, "Aunt Annel would like to have you stay with her for a while. She has a room free now." I almost shouted with joy. I had always wanted to spend some time with Aunt Annel.

Aunt Annel really was my great-aunt. She was my father's favorite, the only relative on my father's side whom I knew. She was the only one who had not turned from him when he married, the only one who had lovingly accepted my mother. My father had lived with her as a young student and later as a young lawyer, because Aunt Annel had a big apartment right behind the National Museum. She rented rooms, furnished, breakfast included. She herself lived only in the kitchen, where she could move along narrow paths between the stove and the cupboard and between her bed and the table. Every available inch was filled with objects, food packages and old newspapers and photograph albums and dishes and boxes of all kinds. Aunt Annel had never in her life thrown out a thing, she had kept them all, because it could happen that one might need something at some point; she knew the exact location of each spool of thread. Her kitchen was full of secrets, just like the attic in the house of my grandparents.

Aunt Annel had never married, and my father often teased her, saying, "No wonder, Aunt Annel—what man would like to live in a kitchen like yours?" Aunt Annel usually patted his hand and replied, "Never you mind, you fresh boy. There were several who would have liked to!" Then she laughed and blushed. She had been a real beauty in her day, my father told me. She still had a cheerful little nose and cheeks like velvet, and a thick brown knot of hair. But her feet in the black button shoes were sometimes tired now and her hands shook.

I moved in with Aunt Annel. The corner room with the

Biedermeier furniture was free: a lady who had lived there for ten years was getting married, and the new tenant would not be arriving until the following month. Aunt Annel received me with open arms. She made a cup of hot chocolate at once; the stove was still warm.

We made ourselves comfortable on the worn black leather sofa. First I had to talk, and Aunt Annel said, "I'm not at all surprised, I can't stand those modern houses either!" I nodded and felt better immediately. It was not a betrayal to confess my unhappiness to Aunt Annel because she loved my parents, too.

Then Aunt Annel began to talk, and her blue eyes grew young again. She talked about the theatre and operettas, her passion. She was an operetta fanatic. She knew all of Strauss and all of Lehár by heart, down to the last note, and I listened attentively to the stories of the Duke of Luxembourg and of the Gypsy Baron and of Friederike. As I drank my hot chocolate I nodded with deep understanding when Aunt Annel sighed and said, "Yes, my whole youth is in those waltzes, child."

Later the two other tenants joined us. Aunt Annel put some more coals on and made some more hot chocolate. The coals crackled in the kitchen stove, and the two ladies had to sit on Aunt Annel's bed because there was no room elsewhere, and they said, "Thank heaven for Miss Annel and her operettas!"

When I returned home some days later, the apartment looked less cold and strange. My room had curtains now—the

familiar curtains from School Street—and I was content and
stopped crying in the night.

Then I had to start in my new school. It was in the
Weinberg section of Prague, but I had to take the streetcar to
get there. I was very proud of my student pass in a blue-framed
plastic case; what would grubby Ernestine say to all that?

Boys and girls sat together in the same classroom, a
change that took some getting used to. The very first morning
one of the Blaha twins tripped me so that I fell on my way to
the blackboard. He was given detention, but that did not help
me much.

The girl who shared the last row with me because we two
were the tallest did not seem to have much compassion for my
anger. Beet-red in the face, she sat motionless, refusing to
answer my questions. Only when noon approached and she
realized that she would soon have to get up did she show me
what had happened. Her light blue skirt was stained with
blood in the back. Terrified, I helped her with her coat so that
no one would see her disgrace. Then I walked her to her
streetcar and tried to steady her; I was worried that she might
faint any minute. But she was very cheerful, and we decided
to be friends. Irene Dvořak had a much bigger bosom than I.
I envied her.

While I waited for my streetcar the loudspeaker in the
lamp post above me coughed in anticipation. Then a trium-
phant voice announced that a heroic U-boat had sunk thirteen
thousand tons in the Atlantic during the night. Then drums
and fifes rendered "We shall bring England to her knees." But

I no longer listened since my streetcar was rattling down the Weinberg Hill with me on board. The young conductor winked at me when I showed him my student pass. I quickly turned away and looked out the window, because I was not quite sure why he was laughing. Was it because I was a girl of almost thirteen, or because he needed some solace after the loudspeaker announcement? In any case, it was not proper to return his laugh.

Slowly I grew used to life in Prague. I stopped being scared of cars, and I even learned to jump off a moving streetcar without falling. It was not hard at all—one just had to lean back as far as possible when jumping. In those early Prague days streetcars were a special joy for me. I spent many afternoons riding from one terminal to the other in order to go for a walk in completely unknown neighborhoods. Only when I began to feel really lonely would I hurry home to give my mother a breathless account of my adventures.

Once I persuaded Irene to come with me because we were friends. But Irene was much more interested in the young men in the streetcar than in walking around terminal stations, and we almost had a fight. Irene said that my journeys were childish, and I told her that she should pull her skirt down over her knees. "Now you're talking just like my mother," Irene said and laughed and made a face. An old lady across the aisle looked at us sternly. Irene started poking me until I too had to laugh.

Irene lived in Straschnitz, another suburb, in a small room behind a tavern owned by her uncle. Irene's mother lived with her; she was divorced and had crippled legs. She sat alone in the room all day, holding an orange-colored guinea pig on her lap. When I came to visit Irene, I would sit with her mother and keep her company. But conversation was difficult; Irene's mother had a whiney voice and the guinea pig constantly dropped little pellets which Irene's mother picked up with her fingers to throw into the wastebasket.

When I tried discussing her mother with Irene, she just shrugged her shoulders. She much preferred helping her uncle in the taproom, where she could joke with the customers and let her skirts fly. Her legs were round and firm. I looked down at my own body. It was all angles, and my bosom was barely visible, even when I pushed my chest out and held my breath. I was very unhappy with myself.

Our apartment turned out to be quite cozy. After checking all the doors and windows, the workmen had departed. The janitor had cleared away the rubble in the backyard and had sowed grass. For the time being the meadow behind the fence looked much greener than his pampered square. Primroses and tiny daisies bloomed in the meadow in profusion, and sometimes toward evening a shepherd brought his flock.

The Giacomelli family had the apartment next to ours. My parents and they became friends. Mr. Giacomelli was an engineer. He was tall, dark, and a bit aloof. He came from the South Tyrol, "That's why he has an Italian name," my mother explained. "And please don't stare at him when he comes to visit!" I blushed and had a coughing fit. Mr. Giacomelli looked like a beautiful young god to me, and I had hoped that nobody would notice. Mrs. Giacomelli was a pretty redhead; she had green eyes and many freckles.

On the sixth floor an efficiency apartment with a terrace housed the Kuchlers. Hilde Kuchler, a distant cousin of my father's, was only nineteen; she was blond and liked to laugh. Her husband, Emil, was not much older. They had only been married since fall, and they always hugged each other as they came down the stairs. Sometimes it sounded as if only one person was descending; they coordinated their steps perfectly.

Above us, on the fourth floor, lived Dr. Rechlitz and his wife. They had also been married only a short time. Dr. Rechlitz worked in the hospital in the suburb of Bohnitz. He left very early in the morning and sometimes came home very late. Mrs. Rechlitz would visit my mother often—because she was a lonely young thing, my mother said. She was cheerful and her mouth was always very red, and her long lashes made pretty shadows on her cheeks. Whenever she spoke of their yearning to have children, she grew sad and said, "All those years we waited because Ludwig was studying, and now we don't have the courage. God knows what will happen to us all." My mother quickly looked in my direction and offered Mrs. Rechlitz some coffee.

Sometimes, when he was off duty, Dr. Rechlitz came along on these visits. His glasses gleamed in a friendly way, he looked me over, and said to my mother, "For heavens sake, what do you feed the girl? She's grown three inches since I last saw her!" Then he would laugh and quickly pull out his pad to prescribe some vitamins for me.

On Sundays Aunt Ella and her husband also came to visit. Aunt Ella was learning English because there was hope again that they might get another visa. Uncle Fred's export business had been taken over by a German manager, who permitted Uncle Fred to work in his own firm as a typist, and that was a great honor, Uncle Fred said. I did not think it was fair, but Uncle Fred patted my shoulder saying, "This is how things are, for the present." There was nothing I could say about that; "for the present" was Uncle Fred's favorite phrase.

The following summer I could not go visit my grandparents because an order had come to vacate the old house on Prague Street within a week; a room had been assigned to them in town. My father took some days off and went to help them move. When he came back, he brought my mother a box filled with yellowed family photographs. She sat over it for a long time, crying. It was all that remained of the attic in the old house.

Jews had been issued stars—two black triangles inscribed at the center with the word *JUDE* printed on yellow fabric. These were to be worn visibly at all times, attached to the left side of the chest. Some had sewn theirs carefully and neatly onto their coats, using many tiny stitches, as if the stars were to remain fixed on the coats for years and years. Others, like Emil Kuchler, attached them sloppily, with safety pins. My mother had sewn her star slightly lower, below her chest, so that when she went out with me or with my father she could hold her handbag over it. Jews and non-Jews were not permitted to walk together.

Once I heard my father laugh angrily as he said, "Maybe you should leave your handbag at home, and I should put on my Iron Cross. That would be funny!" I grew frightened.

Surely it would not be funny at all but terribly dangerous. What would the Germans say? But it had only been a joke; the Iron Cross First Class stayed in its box, and my mother continued holding her handbag over her star when they next went for a walk.

The maneuver did not seem at all strange to me, it was a common practice. Mrs. Giacomelli's star was also sewn below her chest. Dr. Rechlitz's was sewn almost under his sleeve; he began to carry his briefcase under his arm even when he was not going to the hospital. Mrs. Rechlitz carried her handbag in her hand as always, because she was an Aryan. She balanced along on spike heels.

Only the Kuchlers from the sixth floor no longer descended the stairs in unison. Emil Kuchler ran to work in the morning as if wild men were chasing him, and once when Hilde Kuchler came to visit her eyes were red-rimmed. My father had a long talk with her in the living room. The door was shut tight, and my mother sent me to my room and closed the door behind me, so that I would not hear a sound. Much later, when they came out again, I heard my father say to Hilde, "In that case it will be better if you don't come to see us again." His voice was very cold and strict. Hilde Kuchler did not speak. I listened at the keyhole and wanted to hear more, but the apartment door closed and my father did not say another word.

I felt sorry for Hilde Kuchler; she had pretty dimples when she laughed, and such pretty blond hair with curls above her forehead. I did not see her for a long time after that, and I was secretly angry with my father; I thought that he had not been very polite; she was his cousin, after all.

Emil Kuchler continued running to work. He did not answer when one said hello to him. His pants were shabby, his shirt collars were grimy, and he never wore a tie. My mother said that Hilde Kuchler was no longer living with him, she was getting a divorce, and that was the reason why Emil Kuchler's clothes were so untidy.

And then one morning there was a commotion on the sixth floor. The janitor rang and knocked and hammered at Emil Kuchler's door, all the while holding a damp handkerchief to his nose. The hallway smelled of gas. Then the janitor went and got the pass-key and unlocked Emil Kuchler's door. The whole house smelled of gas. The previous night Emil Kuchler had sat down in his kitchenette and had turned on all the burners.

He was buried in the Jewish cemetery. Only my mother and Mrs. Giacomelli and Dr. Rechlitz were there, because Emil Kuchler had come from Germany and had no family of his own. Aryans were not permitted to attend funerals of Jews.

Hilde Kuchler later returned to the efficiency apartment. Her name was Hilde Leidel now, and the apartment had been freshly repainted. The smell of gas, the janitor had said, you could not get it out with fresh air alone, paint was what you had to have. Hilde Kuchler worked at the Reich Protection Ministry. Sometimes in the morning, when we sat at the breakfast table, I would hear her running down the stairs. I knew her step, and my father must have known it, too. He always frowned and pushed away his coffee cup.

One evening when I went to get my father's beer, I saw

a gray military car stopping in front of our house. I froze, because a military car could not mean anything but danger. I crept under the stairs, pressing the jug against my chest; my heartbeats sounded even louder against the porcelain. Then I could see that there was no danger: Hilde Kuchler was coming up the steps, moving toward the elevator, with a German officer. He was young and very happy. His arm around her hips, he said, "Who would want to be that fussy?" Hilde Kuchler laughed as she opened the elevator door. Before the door fell shut and the elevator slowly began to move, the ceiling light fell on her blond curls and on the officer's silvery shoulders. I waited for the elevator to arrive on the sixth floor. Doors were opened and shut, and then the elevator came down again, empty and dark. It stopped with a shudder, and everything was quiet. I went across the street to get the beer; I never told my parents what I had seen.

Then Ernestine came to visit me. She was freshly scrubbed and was wearing a new dress which did not have any spots on the sleeve, and she had a dozen new handkerchiefs in her suitcase. But otherwise she was still dumb old Ernestine. She gaped because we lived on the third floor and because she had never seen a house with so many people in it and because she had never seen a streetcar before and never so many cars and never an elevator and never a mother who wore a star on her coat and held her handbag over it.

For a while Ernestine's gaping was fun. I took her to the Castle and pulled her up the five hundred and sixty-seven steps to the bell tower of the Cathedral. I took her on the streetcar from one terminal to another. Eventually, however, Ernestine was just too dumb. All she ever did was gape; she understood nothing. By the time Irene Dvořak wrinkled her nose and said that Ernestine's hair was too stringy and that she did not smell too nice besides—by then I had already given up on Ernestine.

My mother was cordial to Ernestine as always. She took me aside and said, "Ernestine is our guest, and you behave accordingly, no matter what Irene Dvořak tells you." I grumbled a lot and was mad at my mother because she did not want to understand that I was grown up now and had no patience with grubby children. The laughter in my mother's eyes faded. "If you're as grown up as you think, then you must be polite." I sighed and went to show Ernestine the Old Town clock, which made her gape for the rest of the afternoon. It was true that she did not smell as nice as Irene.

But the week Ernestine was to spend with us passed quickly. In her dumb state she did not even notice that I could not wait to be rid of her. In the railroad station she kept embracing me and promised again and again to write to me every day. I had not even asked her to, she was that dumb.

Walking home from the station I felt alone and misunderstood. But my mother came and hugged me and said, "Here comes my heroine who handles herself so well!" I could see that she had understood me all week long, and I was quite pleased. Nevertheless I made a mad face.

"I am going to tell Papa on you," I said, "and he will not let you have any butter for breakfast!"

Then we both giggled and hugged one another. The breakfast butter was our family joke. My mother received Jewish ration cards. *JUDE JUDE JUDE* was printed all over them in big black letters. She had to sign her name on them, Marie Sara Richter, although Sara was not her name at all. The Germans had ordered that every Jewish woman had to call herself Sara. All my mother received in exchange for these ration cards was some margarine. And we shared our Aryan butter with her every morning.

Aunt Ella did not come very often now, but I went to see her almost every day. Since she no longer worked in an office, she had learned pastry-making. "We'll certainly have more use for something of that kind in America than for accounting," she said. There was hope again that they might get another visa. She spent every morning standing in one of the lines at the American Embassy.

But in the afternoons Aunt Ella practiced what she had learned from her chef patissier; she made tiny cream rolls and cornucopias, and light green and pink-colored fondant, and I watched her nimbly mix almond paste from the black market and move the tip of her tongue from one corner of her mouth to the other. I sat very still as I watched, quietly handing Aunt Ella pans and spoons. Sometimes I was allowed to grate hazelnuts from the black market or put chocolate from the black market into the double boiler. I would not have gone away for anything in the world, although watching and helping was torture; we were not permitted to taste a single one of the pastries, not a single one of the bonbons. The baker weighed all the ingredients twice before giving them to Aunt Ella, and she had to bring back exactly the same weight in finished pieces. Sometimes, when the sugar did not melt properly, she would be beside herself. She would have tears in her eyes and call out in a tearful voice, "Please come and help me, Daddy!" And Daddy—Uncle Fred—would get up from his solitaire, take off his glasses, sniff, and pretend that he understood a lot about how pastries were made. But he did not really understand much, I knew, because usually he only said, "You have to wait and be calm, child, for the present." Then he would kiss Aunt Ella and go back to his solitaire game.

Aunt Ella would weep and sigh a while longer, but then the sugar usually did what she wanted it to, dripping downward like a long silvery thread. Aunt Ella would wipe her nose with the back of her hand and cheer up.

Uncle Fred was always home now, the German manager had learned everything from him and no longer needed him. He sat around the apartment playing solitaire. His elegant English suits were hanging loosely on him, and the collars of his silk shirts no longer hugged his throat. When it rained, he always coughed a good deal. Sometimes my mother sent him some milk because she was on friendly terms with the lady from the dairy shop. This always caused Uncle Fred to remark, "Your mother should feed you, Helenka, for the present." Then he would argue with Aunt Ella for a long time, insisting that she drink some of the milk. Aunt Ella was always reluctant at first. Only when Uncle Fred stated, "Then I will not have any either, child," would Aunt Ella give in and drink a little. But she cheated every time by taking tiny sips.

But then they did not get a visa after all. Aunt Ella stopped going to the American Embassy and began to make fondant candies and marzipan mushrooms and chocolate cups even in the mornings. Sugar dripped into the iron pan, Aunt

Ella's tongue wandered from one corner of her mouth to the other, and Uncle Fred coughed.

Once as I was coming home from school, the loudspeaker above the streetcar stop rattled again before the voice announced that our heroic Japanese allies had destroyed Pearl Harbor. I did not know where Pearl Harbor was, but the voice said that Germany had declared war on America; Pearl Harbor must be in America, I thought. Thank heavens Aunt Ella had not gone there, she might be dead now.

When the streetcar came the passengers did not look as grouchy as usual after loudspeaker announcements. The conductor laughed, bent down to me, and whispered, "The Americans will show them!" I nodded without quite knowing what the Americans were supposed to show and to whom: Japan was at the other end of the world! But maybe what had happened was a good thing after all. Maybe it was too bad that Aunt Ella and Uncle Fred had not gone to America.

I returned to school after lunch for gym three times a week. Once the streetcar was stopped by four soldiers wearing skulls and bones on their caps. They stormed inside, each into one compartment, and demanded to see our papers. The soldiers, who were holding guns in their hands, omitted no one. A man wearing a star stood on the outside platform—the only place where Jews were allowed to ride. He was eager to show his papers, but the soldiers slapped and hit him and took him away. He looked back once, very calmly, as if expecting that someone would come to his defense. But all the people in the streetcar looked straight ahead, each one for himself, as if nothing had happened. Then the conductor rang the bell and the streetcar rumbled on.

That afternoon the gym class was canceled. We were made to sit in the classroom for a long time. Then Hlawitza, the German professor, came in. He wore his black boots and he was even paler than usual, and he shouted that they would find the guilty person, the cowardly dog, the Jew-Bolshevik, they would certainly find the man who that very afternoon had shot Reichsprotector Heydrich in the back and killed him. Then we all went home.

I woke up in the middle of the night. There were light and noise and heavy steps on the stairs. Our doorbell rang and someone shouted, "Open up!" I crept back into bed and pulled my blanket over my head. I heard my father go to the door. I pushed the blanket away from my face: if my father was not afraid, I could not be afraid either. Two soldiers with guns and skulls came in, the janitor running after them, wearing his nightgown and shaking, and he said, "Dr. Richter lives here!" But the soldiers did not want my father at all, they did not want my mother either, and I began to breathe again. They merely opened all the doors and all the closets, and they looked under each of the beds. One of them had dirt on his boots. The other one came into my room, he smelled of sweat, and he looked under my bed and picked up my blanket. I held it tight around my neck. He looked at me, then he turned away and said, "The hell with it all!" Then they left. They rang the bell next door, I heard the janitor say, "Mr. Giacomelli lives here!" Then my mother came in and said, "I'm going to make some tea." She went into the kitchen.

My father patted my hand, which was still clutching the blanket. Now I could let go. I asked, "What did they want?"

My father looked at me as if he had just woken up. His eyes were frightened now. He was amazed that I did not understand. "They are looking for the murderer," he said. "But come now, we'll have some tea." We sat on our kitchen stools and drank tea from the breakfast coffee cups. My parents did not speak.

Two days later my mother's hands were shaking as she told me that they had found the murderers. They had come from England, she said, with parachutes, and I should go to town and look at the church where they had been hiding.

Irene and I went together. The front of the church was scarred by many bullet holes, the windows were all broken, and the doors were boarded up. A soldier who was standing guard told us to stop loitering and to keep moving. Irene made eyes at him, but I took her arm and pulled her away.

I admired Irene more than ever, because she was in love now. In the mornings, before she went to class, she would stand in the washroom for hours, making faces and pulling at her hair. She buckled her belt so tightly that it looked as if instead of a waist she had an empty space between her chest and her hips. She had bought herself a small round box of makeup, and I had to keep it for her in my satchel. Irene moaned, "If my uncle finds it, he'll give me a beating!" Since my mother never went through my things, I could keep the makeup for Irene. Every morning before school I brought it to the washroom.

Irene was in love with Josef Nedoma. He sat on the boys'

bench in the back and I liked him too, because he was tall and blond and had a deep voice, not a squeaky one like the others. Marie Schneider sat two rows further up. She had many pimples and did Josef Nedoma's homework because she loved him, too. But Josef Nedoma had chosen Irene, although he continued to take his homework off Marie. I did not think he was being fair, but Irene only laughed. She wrote love letters under her desk, rolled them into balls, and threw them to Josef Nedoma. He wrote too, and his ears turned red. As soon as Professor Nemecek turned to the blackboard, paper balls started flying back and forth. I had to write Irene's papers because she simply did not have the time.

Josef Nedoma did not have a father any more, and his mother was working somewhere or other. One day Irene told me that after gym we would be going to visit Josef Nedoma in his apartment. He lived in a row house in the Old Quarter, where the stairs smelled of cabbage. Josef Nedoma's apartment consisted only of a kitchen with two sofas in it. Josef Nedoma and Irene sat on one sofa and I sat on the other, right next to the sink. Josef Nedoma pulled a blanket over his and Irene's heads, and Irene giggled under the blanket.

For a while I watched the blanket heaving over their heads and hands, but then I grew bored and went to stand at the window. Irene giggled. Next door a woman was shaking out a thick shag rug; dust tickled her nose and she sneezed. Down in the yard little kids were playing blind man's buff. The kitchen clock ticked very slowly, the faucet dripped. I went over to the sink and tightened the tap. Then I went back to the window. The woman was still sneezing.

After a while Irene and Josef Nedoma came out from under the blanket, both looking disheveled; Josef Nedoma's ears were very red. Irene combed her hair in front of the mirror over the sink. Josef Nedoma carefully folded the blanket. Then we left. Irene's cheeks were hot. She hugged me in the hallway and said, "Next time we'll take Paul Kunert with us, then you'll have fun, too." I shrugged. I didn't especially like Paul Kunert. He had crooked teeth.

But I went with them the next time. The clock again ticked slowly. Because there was only one blanket, all of us had to fit on one sofa. Josef Nedoma and Irene kissed like movie stars and sighed a lot. Paul Kunert kissed me, but his crooked teeth were in his way. I let him kiss me because I was squeezed between him and Irene and I did not want to be a spoilsport. The blanket over our heads stifled our breath, it was hot, and Paul Kunert's crooked teeth were everywhere.

Then Josef Nedoma suggested that we, the girls, should take off our dresses. His mother would not be home for a long time. Irene giggled and agreed. I said no, and Paul Kunert turned red and said no. It was a tie, two against two, and so Josef Nedoma folded the blanket again and we went home.

Outside I told Irene that I would not come to Josef Nedoma's apartment again. I still felt the hot blanket on my face and Paul Kunert's crooked teeth, and I was angry at myself. Irene said, "All right, then I'll take Marie Schneider with me!"

We did not speak to each other for a week after that. In the morning I put the small round makeup box on the sink without a word, and Irene returned it without a word after she had put the makeup on her cheeks. Eventually both of us grew tired of the charade, and we made up. Irene went alone to Josef Nedoma's after that, and I continued doing her papers for her.

Professor Hlawitza hated me, a condition that caused me great suffering. I was not a grind, but I liked my teachers to like me. Even in first grade I had always felt good when old Mrs. Dolezal patted my head as she walked past my bench. At first I could not understand why Hlawitza either looked at me angrily or completely ignored me. I was good in German, and I could have been his best student if he had only let me. I secretly learned grammar rules and parsed sentences, but he very rarely called on me. He would joke with the others once in a while, but he only sneered at me. He had pale cheeks under shifty eyes, and his hands were pale and thin; his wife, Irene said, had a baby every year.

Once I stayed behind in the classroom during the mid-morning break to copy Irene's algebra for her. At last all the examples were done, and I hurried to get outside. In the door I almost bumped into Hlawitza. He looked down at me, his eyes were evil even close up, and he reached up and pulled my hair so hard that my head hit the doorframe. He hissed, "Damn brat!" I mumbled an apology and ran downstairs. In all my life nobody had called me "damn brat." When I told Irene she just shrugged. "Never mind him," she said, "you know he's a Nazi!" Her head was full of Josef Nedoma, and she had little patience with me.

My mother wanted to know what had happened to make me unhappy. When I told her, I hoped she would be very angry about mean old Hlawitza and would tell my father about him. I had hoped that my father would go to my school at once to defend me and punish Hlawitza. But my mother only said, "Stay away from him if he doesn't like you." That was all. My father also acted as if nothing had happened, but I was sure he knew; my mother always told him everything.

So I continued sitting mute through all the German lessons, deserted by everyone. I knew all the answers and said them quietly to myself. But I was rarely called on. When Hlawitza did ask me something, his voice was cutting and sarcastic, and the class dutifully giggled.

Toward the end of the school year I was returning some maps to the conference room after geography class. It was not until I had placed them all on the table and was turning to leave that I noticed Hlawitza standing by the paper supplies. He had not answered the door. I ducked, thinking that he would hit me. But Hlawitza lifted my chin with one finger and said, "Oh, nice little Miss Richter, who is always so good!" I tried to smile, but the meanness in his voice made me tremble. He still would not let me go, his eyes traveled from my face downward to my thin checkered blouse with pockets on my chest. He lifted one of the pocket flaps with two fingers and said, "A pretty blouse—" but then his fingers were no longer on my blouse but on my breast. I stammered something, pushed him aside and ran out. The conference room door slammed. Only when I got to the end of the corridor did I collect myself: I caught my breath and returned to the classroom.

This episode was not at all like Paul Kunert with his

crooked teeth under Josef Nedoma's blanket. Paul Kunert was a pal, and he had meant well. What had happened now was evil and mean and disgusting, black riding boots and a baby every year.

I did not tell Irene. At lunch, when I could not swallow a single bite, I told my mother. She did not look at me. Then she touched my head. I could not see her face. She said, "I thought it would be something like this, from the very beginning. I will tell Papa."

I expected my father to go to the principal's office the very same day to destroy Hlawitza with a single sentence. I hated Hlawitza now the same way he hated me. A teacher was not allowed to do a thing like that, that I knew, and I wanted my father to avenge me. But my father did not go to the principal's office. He acted as if nothing had happened and played chess. He did not do anything the next day, and he must have known what had happened: my mother always told him everything.

I felt humiliated and ashamed for him. He had always been my hero, he had been a proud man afraid of no one, he had been more handsome and more intelligent than all the other fathers. The three of us were supposed to stick together no matter what happened. Why wasn't he defending his daughter now? But my father did not speak, and his eyes were afraid now, afraid as they had been when we were leaving the small town in Moravia. I had never seen so much fear in my father's eyes. He had always been my hero. Why was he a hero no longer?

Several days later my mother spoke to me. "There's nothing we can do," she said. "You'll simply have to avoid the man as best you can." But by then my father had already ceased being a hero for me. He had done nothing but play chess.

We spent that summer in Prague. My mother was not permitted to ride the trains, and my father did not feel like taking a vacation. Toward the end of the summer I went with him to visit my grandparents, just for one week. My mother stayed home. She waved to us from the window for a long time.

Grandfather met us at the station as always, and for a fleeting moment everything was as it had been, the begonia baskets above the platforms and the framed sign, "Altitude: 582 meters above sea level." But when I got a close look at grandfather, I was startled. He was bent over and looked tired, and the star on his coat was like a mark of shame. He whispered to my father that he would rather walk behind us. I didn't understand his reasons: I turned and smiled and waved to him, but grandfather did not wave back. His eyes were fixed on the ground. And suddenly I remembered: Jews and non-Jews were not allowed to walk together, not even here. My grandfather held his head low as he walked behind us, and he did not speak to anyone. Some people we met greeted him in a loud voice, and some looked away as if they were ashamed.

This time we went to the town square because we were to live in the hotel. It was the same hotel which had once housed grandfather's drivers and which had later been called Hotel Löwy. Now its name was Post-Hotel. Grandfather waited outside while we took our bags in because Jews were not permitted to enter. My father held my hand. The manager, Mr. Uher, gave us our room key and whispered, "It's a rotten shame, Dr. Richter, a rotten shame." He looked through the window at grandfather's bent back, and then he pulled out his handkerchief and blew his nose for a long time. Following us to the sidewalk, he said, "How are you, Mr. Löwy?" But grandfather did not answer him.

My grandparents were rooming at the Weiners'. Mr. Weiner had once been grandfather's accountant, but he had retired a long time ago. The apartment was narrow and dark. The Weiners had given their best room to my grandparents, although grandfather had not ever associated with them much: Mr. Weiner had been the Eldest in the Jewish Community, and I had often heard my grandfather say that he himself did not like all those people who thought of themselves as Jews rather than Czechs.

Grandmother and Mrs. Weiner now kept house together. A year before, when my grandparents had moved in, my father told me, they had tried to cook separately. But the kitchen was much too small for two families, there were not enough pans for two separate meals, and Mrs. Weiner was not fond of cooking, anyway. So grandmother had taken over the cooking for all of them, and Mrs. Weiner, sighing copiously, did all the dishes. My grandmother still wore the black velvet ribbon around her neck. Many tiny wrinkles fanned out below her eyes, and the blue eyes themselves held all the sadness. She wore one of Emma's old aprons as she cooked. She could have wrapped herself in it twice over.

For supper there still was my favorite dish, Wiener schnitzel. Mr. Brichta, the butcher, personally brought a small package of meat every second night. He kept it hidden under his coat and would not accept money. He brought it, he said, for the sake of the good old days. The egg lady also came frequently, a bag over her arm. Sometimes a pound of butter or a package of flour would be on the doorstep, and grandmother would not know whom to thank for it. Only the wine cream was missing, because all the wine had remained in the cellar of the old house. But I did not mention it, nor did anyone else.

I was now old enough, even grandmother had to agree, to be allowed to roam about on my own. I went to the castle and in the opposite direction, where the forest began. Sometimes I would meet grandfather's friends. They said, "Look here, the Löwy granddaughter!" Then they would inquire after my grandparents. I told them that grandmother spent a lot of time cooking and that grandfather would not talk to anyone, not even to me. Then they patted my shoulder, said, "Oh yes, oh yes," and walked on quickly.

Once I went to visit Franziska. She lived in a development behind the railroad because her husband now worked for the sugar factory. She had grown chubby and had twins. She embraced me and bawled a bit and said, "You are almost big enough now to get married!" I pinched her arm as I had always done. The twins crawled around in the grass and drooled a great deal.

Franziska sat down on the garden bench and picked up one twin. But the other one began to scream right away because he wanted to be picked up too. Franziska was laughing again and holding them both. Her lap was large enough. Then she said, "Your grandmother gave me all her linen to keep for you. You have to tell your mother that everything is here. If she needs something, I will send it."

I wanted to ask Franziska whether she still thought of the handsome trumpet player. Then I decided not to.

Franziska told me that old Emma had died the previous winter. "She had a beautiful death," she nodded, "she lay down at night and was dead in the morning, all peaceful, too. She never was quite right after she had to leave the old house. She missed it a lot." Franziska sighed and used her apron to wipe away the twins' drool. Both babies had black eyes just like Franziska's husband.

I thought of old Emma, of her legs in the thick woolen stockings walking ahead of me toward the iron attic door, of the dry-hot attic air . . .

"I want to give you some sugar to take to your grandmother," said Franziska. "Tell her she only has to let me know when she needs more, we have plenty of it." She put the twins down in the grass again. They were drooling more than before. Then she got up, straightened her apron, and went inside.

Only on the last day of our stay did I secretly go to see the old house. I had overheard grandmother telling my father that it was still standing empty, although they had been forced to move out in a hurry one year ago. She thought standing empty would damage the thick old walls for sure.

The house looked strange. The shutters were closed and the pebbled path leading to the three steps under the glass veranda was overgrown with weeds. Nothing moved. Grass stood knee-high, or bent sadly to the side where rain had flattened it. I could see the green lawn swing between the trees, but the weathervane was no longer on its roof. It had been loose last time already; the wind had probably torn it off. The silver firs nodded at the garden gate, and in the large bed, underneath the many weeds, there was an occasional red shimmer: grandfather's strawberries.

Next door, in Sonia's garden, there were voices. Someone was living in Sonia's house. I looked carefully; three boys were playing on the lawn. They wore black corduroy shorts with little daggers at their belts, swastikas were sewn on the sleeves of their brown shirts, and swastikas decorated the medals on their chests. The hedge between the two gardens was high and thick: the narrow pass-through had grown over.

That night we had to say goodbye to my grandparents. Our train was to leave early in the morning, and grandfather could not accompany us to the station because Jews were not allowed out so early. Grandmother held me for a long time. I felt her pulse under the black velvet ribbon. She said, "Please take good care of your mother." I nodded, and over grandmother's shoulder I saw my grandfather holding my father's hands. The bent shoulders of my grandfather were shaking—he was crying. I had never thought that my grandfather could cry, tears were running down his cheeks. No, I could not look at that. I tore myself away from grandmother and ran outside.

In the morning we returned to Prague. Nobody accompanied us. "It's as if they were gone already," my father said.

But the begonia baskets above the platforms moved slightly as always.

I was glad to be back in Prague, where I did not have to live in a hotel which was no longer named Hotel Löwy, where there was no old house, and no strange boys in Sonia's garden, and no grandmother in Emma's old apron, and no grandfather who would not speak any more and who had cried so terribly. I did not talk about our visit and kept quiet no matter how much they asked me.

"You should not have let her go," said Aunt Ella to my mother on her next visit. "She is barely fourteen, she has enough problems with her own self." But my mother shook her head very firmly. "Let her see it all," she said. "Just let her see everything. Someone will have to know about it later on."

Aunt Ella looked at my mother for a long time. Then she put her hand on my mother's hand, looked in my direction, and whispered, "Don't talk like that!"

Then my mother told me that Uncle Fritz's family was in a transport. I asked her where they were having themselves transported to. I thought of a train of shiny Humbers, it sounded like an adventure. But my mother said that nobody knew, it would be one of the first transports. And she added that I would have to give little Paul my ski boots to wear because it would be cold soon.

But I did not like Paul, Uncle Fritz's oldest grandson. He had always been sneering and conceited. Why should I have to give him my beautiful ski boots? I said, no, of course I would not, I still needed my ski boots, even though I could not wear thick socks with them any more and even though

they made my big toe hurt. But my mother said that Paul
would need the ski boots more than I. I was angry. Did my
mother really care more about Paul's feet than about mine?
But there was no help for it. My mother insisted that I come
with her to deliver the ski boots and to say goodbye.

I shouted and carried on and told my mother that I did
not like her any more. The following afternoon we went to
Uncle Fritz's. Suitcases and rucksacks were all over the apartment; instead of the Warnsdorf Persian rugs, thin rags covered
the parquet floors.

Uncle Fritz said that they had traded all they owned for
provisions and warm clothing; and that again made it sound
as if they were setting out on an adventure. But they all had
numbers sewn above their stars.

Stupid Paul put on my beautiful ski boots, he had to put
on two pairs of thick socks first so that his feet would not slide
in them. He exclaimed, "They fit perfectly!" and looked at me
with a smirk. Then he buckled the beautiful buckles which had
once been my whole pride. He did not even say thank-you.
I embraced Aunt Elsa, wondering whether she had already
packed the pink fan of ostrich feathers. Later, when I asked my
mother, she looked at me in astonishment. "I doubt it," she
said.

We did not have word from Uncle Rudolf for a long
time. One night two men in leather coats had come to fetch
him, for questioning, they had said. Two days later an unknown boy had come to Aunt Irma and had asked for Uncle
Rudolf's shaving kit and a change of underwear. That was the
last we heard. Aunt Irma fell ill, she had always had a weak

constitution, and Uncle Rudolf remained absent. No one mentioned him, and everyone acted as if he had never existed. And then one day a postcard from him arrived, it came from Prague, it came from the Palais Petchek, and the Palais Petchek was, as everyone knew, the headquarters of the Gestapo. Uncle Rudolf asked my mother to bring him a change of underwear.

My mother went to Aunt Irma to pick up the underwear, and in the afternoon she took me with her to the Palais Petchek.

The man stationed at the front entrance asked, "What do you want?", and the skull on his cap was grinning. My mother showed him Uncle Rudolf's postcard and her papers, and I showed him my monthly streetcar pass. He looked at us with disgust and let us in. My mother held my hand so tightly that it hurt as we walked up some steps to another guard. He also asked, "What do you want?" and we showed the postcard and the papers and my streetcar pass. Then we had to stand against a wall and wait for a long time. My mother clutched my hand, and I stroked the back of her wrist with my thumb. She was holding onto the package with Uncle Rudolf's underwear so tightly with her other hand that her knuckles turned white. The star on her coat moved up and down, up and down with her heartbeats.

Then another skull came and impatiently gestured to us to follow him. He said, "Get moving!" We ran down the stairs after him. His boots clattered on the stone steps—there were hobnails in the soles. Next to us the one-man elevator hummed, but it was only for men in uniform. I loved to ride these contraptions because they had no doors and you could run in and out of them. But their operation had been forbidden in ordinary houses in town: we had to save electricity. Downstairs the skull said to me, "You wait here, and don't move!" He said to my mother, "You get in here!" My mother let go of my hand and disappeared through the door behind him.

My hand was hurting, why did my mother have to press me so hard? Then another skull came down the corridor, and behind him limped a thin old man in striped pajamas. Both went into the room where my mother had gone before.

I waited and did exercises with my hand. The corridor was very quiet. I cracked my knuckles the way one of the Blaha twins had taught me. The sound echoed in the quiet hall.

Then the second skull came out, and the thin old man in striped pajamas followed him. He was clutching the package now, and he looked at me as he limped past. Would he bring the package to Uncle Rudolf? Then our skull came out and my mother after him. The skull said, "Get moving," and my mother again started to press my hand. I thought, tonight I won't be able to write, and I'm supposed to do my English homework.

The guard upstairs returned the papers and my streetcar pass. We went down to the door, through the door, we were outside. My mother took a deep breath, red spots glowed on her cheeks and neck, and she was still holding onto me. At the corner she halted and said, "Did you see Uncle Rudolf?"

"No, where was he?"

Then we stared at each other. My mother nodded. "Yes, that was Uncle Rudolf," she said.

A man went past, and he whispered to us, "Don't hang around here, do you want them to lock you up?"

My mother took my hand again and pulled me away. I was still staring at her, and she said, "They wanted his signature because of the Bucarest factories." Then we walked silently past the municipal park. The previous night's rain had left the leaves glistening. After a while my mother said, "Remember that well."

I nodded, but my head was still spinning. How could Uncle Rudolf look like that? Was it really he? Then we waited for the streetcar. When it came, I stood with my mother out on the platform; Jews were not permitted to ride inside. I saw the shiny Humber and the chauffeur in his pale blue uniform, and I saw Uncle Rudolf putting his arm around my grandfather, saying, "Nobly shall we perish, my dear Max!"

Some weeks later, during biology class, the school principal came to our classroom. I was writing as much as my notebook would hold about the vertebrae of tadpoles. The principal asked me to collect my things and come to his office at once. I looked at Irene and shrugged my shoulders, and she whispered, "What did you do now, you poor thing?" I shook my head; my conscience was altogether clear. I packed my things; my biology essay was not quite done, I had not written all there was to write about tadpoles. I would have to finish tomorrow. I closed my desk, winked at Irene, and went out.

The principal was waiting outside the door, and that was very strange. He coughed and cleared his throat before speaking. "We have received an order," he said, "by which all Jewish mongrels must leave school immediately. That concerns you, Miss Richter. I am sorry." He took off his glasses and began to polish them.

I said, "Yes, thank you."

I had to go back to the classroom one more time because I had left my coat. While Irene waved to me, all the others looked at me, a question on their faces. They were still staring as I quietly closed the door again. Slowly I walked downstairs and out the big gate.

Leo Jelinek, from the eleventh grade, was hanging around outside. He said, "I didn't know that you were one, too." And I answered, "Sure!" Then I began to run because I could feel the tears rising; there was no need for Leo Jelinek to see them.

My mother cut the star off her coat, put on her hat, and went to find a school that would have me—a private school. I sat crying in my room and said that I would never, never go to any school again if they treated me that way. My father said that a private school might be rather expensive, and, anyway, was it legal?

But my mother looked very determined. "When one is fifteen," she said, "one has to go to school every morning, expensive or not!"

When she came back home, she brought booklets and folders. There were art schools, fashion schools, language schools, and schools for crafts. I wiped my tears and began to take an interest. We decided that I should attend a language school to perfect my English.

That was how I came to be registered in the Lawichka Language School. That same night my mother sewed her star back on her coat.

The Language School was on the fifth floor of a house in the New Section of Prague, not far from Wenceslas Square. The elevator cage was made of wrought iron, and all the doors had very shiny brass knobs. There were three classrooms—French, Italian, and English—a dark corridor, and the director's small office at the far end of it. There Harry Lawichka sat under pictures of horses, poring over racing forms from morning to night. On Monday mornings we could always tell exactly whether his horse had done well at the track that weekend or whether it had disappointed him. His face told the whole story.

In the English room three students were deeply immersed in passive verbs. Mr. Kohler, the teacher, introduced me. To me he said, "With your permission, I will continue to base my teaching on German, Miss Richter." His nose was just like Uncle Fred's, and his Czech sounded abominable.

Right after the first lesson I questioned the girl next to me about Mr. Kohler's family tree. I had become very conscious of Aryan and Jewish descent. The girl laughed a lot before she said, "We're all mongrels here; I bet Mr. Kohler is no exception. But he won't tell us. I am half-Jewish, and little Ilse over there is too. Are you?"

I nodded happily. The girl's name was Susi Renner, and I liked her tremendously. She had warm brown eyes and a dimple in her chin. Suddenly I felt myself belonging to the community of half-Jews. I had been alone before. I had known that there must be more like me, but I had never met them. Even Harry Lawichka was half-Jewish, Susi said, and so was the French teacher, next door. Mrs. Zettler, who was pure American and who practiced conversation with us from eleven to twelve, was married to one. Suddenly the world was full of us. I was delighted with the thought that I belonged somewhere. At lunch, between bites of fruit dumpling, I told my mother about my joy, and she was happy for me.

I could barely wait for the next morning. I wanted to see Susi Renner again and to hear her cheerful voice. Right before the grammar lesson I asked her if we could be friends. She winked at me and said, "If you absolutely insist. But watch out —I'm a dangerous woman!" My laughter was so loud that Mr. Kohler said, "Ladies, I beg your pardon!"

Susi Renner was sixteen. She was much more intelligent than I, and she wrote poetry. And she was no longer a virgin. A year ago she had been in love, she told me—actually she still loved the man, she said—and he had told her that it was old-fashioned to be a virgin. So she had given up being one. She shrugged her shoulders, smoothed her shiny brown hair, and laughed. She had a pretty mouth, graceful shoulders, and a way of walking which I tried in vain to imitate by practicing at home. The man with whom she was still in love was a captain in the German Army.

This part of her confession upset me deeply. For days I thought only about Susi. Until now German uniforms had meant danger and nothing else. Was it really possible to fall in love with them?

Susi lived with her father, who was Jewish and who had

been a professor of Greek. They lived in a one-room apartment in the Weinberg section, having moved from a small town in the north which they had had to leave a year ago. Susi's mother was German, and she was still teaching there because the authorities had not let her move to Prague with her family. "If my Mom were here, I bet I wouldn't be so immoral," Susi said.

Susi's father never left the house. He read all day long. Twice a week a friend brought him books from the university library. A shy and absent-minded man, small of stature, he was completely under Susi's thumb. "My father melts when I make eyes at him," she said, and I nodded in admiration. My father had melted, too, when he met Susi.

Only my mother was skeptical. She did not like the way Susi walked, and she did not like the way Susi batted her eyelashes. My mother had always been honest with me, and she was honest this time as well. But for the first time in my life I objected vehemently. Secretly I thought, "You'd be even more amazed, Mama, if you knew! Susi still loves him, and he is a captain in the German army!" I had never before kept anything from my mother. Now I was glutted with secrets.

Susi was a member of the Nazi Girls' Union. "They forgot to throw me out," she said. She had brought her uniform to Prague, and she continued going to meetings and ball games at the Nazi gym. "You don't belong with them, Susi, why do you go?" I asked, horrified. Susi wore swastikas on her brown uniform jacket; the boys who had played in Aunt Klara's garden had worn them on their brown shirts. But Susi answered, "Of course I belong there. It's not our fault that we're half-Jews, is it?" So I went with her to the next meeting. I could not let her go alone: we were friends.

But the meeting was not horrible at all. Girls wearing white blouses sat around a table, knitting and singing folk songs. The tiled stove was warm and cozy. Since I did not know many of the songs, I dutifully studied the texts. When it was time to go, the leader announced that instead of meeting in the rooms the following week, we would go to a military hospital to sing for our wounded soldiers.

That was the day my mother went to the Prague fair grounds; my grandparents were there as part of a transport that was being assembled, and she was hoping that she could see them one more time. She spent the entire day waiting before the gates. It was very cold. Not until late afternoon did one of the attendants pass on her message, which brought grandmother to the gate. They could talk through the bars. But after two minutes a policeman sent my grandmother back again. She had looked well, my mother said, and I saw that she was trying to comfort herself as well as me. She was only worried about grandfather, because he would not speak. And the people with skulls always wanted the answers very quickly.

I did not need a uniform to go singing in the military hospital, only a dirndl dress and white kneesocks. I did not have a dirndl dress, but Susi had two. We changed at her house. The dress was a bit loose in the waist because I was still a skinny thing and Susi was all curves. But I pulled the apron strings tighter to conceal the sag. I looked very Aryan and was pleased with myself.

Susi's father looked up from his book. His eyes were a warm brown just like Susi's, and he had a nice smile. He asked, "Where are you going?" Susi kissed him and answered, "Oh, just for a walk."

Going down the stairs I looked at Susi. I hoped that she would speak. But Susi danced her way down. She smoothed her shiny hair and said, " 'He who has no house now will not build . . .' Oh, I just adore Rilke! We're going to read his poems together."

We met the others in front of the military hospital. I held Susi's hand so tightly that she shook me. "You'll squoosh me, be careful!" I let go of her, startled: for a moment I thought of my mother who had held on to me the same way. But then I threw back my head. Why should I be thinking of my mother now? I had a right to belong.

We left our coats in a room full of wheelchairs and crutches and wire cages. A nurse led us into a large hall equally full of wheelchairs and crutches. Men without legs were sitting in the wheelchairs, and men with bandages were leaning on the crutches. One had no face, only bandages; he could not see us, and he could not possibly hear us, and one of them had no hands at all. We stood in a semicircle and sang a song about our home in the green mountains. We sang a song about a hazelnut bush that bore brown fruit, and a song about a cool mountain spring, and one of them had a face that was all blue and had lost its nose, and all of them were very young. We sang "Hollara," and the ones who could still smile smiled, and the ones who still had hands clapped. We sang "There by the Village Fountain" and "My Beautiful Homeland" in perfect harmony, and the nurses blew their noses. Then we put our coats back on and left. Outside, the leader snapped her arm upward and said, "Heil Hitler. Until next week," and she walked off with long, self-assured steps. Susi and I took the trolley. We both wept all the way home because the soldiers had been so young.

I changed into my own clothes at Susi's house and folded the white kneesocks carefully. At home my mother looked up from her mending and asked, "Where did you go today?" and I said, "Oh, just for a walk." Then I went to my room and wept some more, because all the soldiers had been so young. I wept also because I knew I had betrayed my mother. I had felt compassion for the others—that was my betrayal.

The only girl in English class who was Aryan was Ilse Wagner. She was twenty-two and in deep mourning. Her hair was brushed very smooth, and she wore two wedding rings on one finger. We felt shy with her because she was a widow and we were merely schoolgirls, but she was always very nice to us and tried to help me when I ran aground over the conditional tenses. Mr. Kohler would then say, "Mrs. Wagner, if I may beg your pardon—" and Ilse Wagner would blush all the way to the roots of her hair, and for a moment her eyes would be full of laughter.

One day she told Susi what had happened to her. Her husband went to the Russian front one week after their wedding, and he died on the first day, somewhere near Sevastopol. Nine months later Ilse's child was born, dead. She told the story in a very quiet voice, only her hands shook as she spoke, Susi said. Then she was sick for a long time, and then her parents sent her to Prague to have a change. Her husband had been a group leader. When I asked what that meant, Susi's eyes grew big as she explained that it made him a member of the SS.

"How did he look?" I asked breathlessly, "Did Ilse Wagner show you a picture?" SS men were all terrible in the Palais Petchek and in Aunt Klara's house; surely Ilse Wagner's husband must have been terrible too.

"Yes, she has one in her wallet," Susi said, "and I tell you, he was simply dreamy."

For a while we looked at one another. Not too many men were dreamy in our eyes. Hannes Stelzer in one of his films was, and Horst Caspar when he played Faust, and sometimes Will Quadflieg would be dreamy for a while in one of his movie roles, and Mozart was dreamy . . .

I told my mother about Ilse Wagner. "Just imagine, Mama, one week after they were married!" I was close to tears with compassion. I did not say anything about his being dreamy.

And my mother answered, "It serves them right, the trash!"

I looked at her and I understood her feelings. But I no longer belonged with her. Ilse Wagner was no trash, she had beautiful hands and was in deep mourning, and she helped me when I got stuck with the conditional tenses; though she knew that she was the only Aryan far and wide, she was always nice to all of us. My mother did not understand, she did not understand anything about Ilse Wagner's terrible sadness. My mother looked at me; then she turned away.

There was another Ilse in our class. She was not yet fifteen and very polite and well-bred. She looked much more Jewish than Susi and I. Mr. Kohler called her Miss Ottenhausen, but that was not her full name. This Ilse who looked so Jewish was really Ilse Stephanie Angelica, Countess von Ottenhausen, and her father was a Count. She once told us all about it in the break, speaking her full name between two bites of her salami sandwich. She said it with such nonchalance that it seemed the simplest thing in the world for a mongrel to have such a name.

Susi and I gaped and asked, "How come?" Ilse shrugged her shoulders. "My father married my mother, she was very rich. But she died when I was little." Then she calmly continued eating her sandwich.

This Ilse came from Berlin. Her house had gone boom there, she said, and her father was at the Finnish front. The old housekeeper, Mrs. Meikle, had simply moved Ilse, and everything that was left in the shelter, to Prague.

Ilse asked whether we wanted to come visit her, and we both nodded: of course we wanted to come. We had never before been guests of a Countess. Usually we did not waste our time with fifteen-year-olds, but Ilse would have to be an exception. We asked whether it would be all right with Mrs. Meikle, and Ilse laughed and said yes, Mrs. Meikle loved company. But we would have to speak up: ever since the night of the bombs something was wrong with her ear, you really had to scream at her.

On a Sunday afternoon we went to pay our visit. The sign on the door read "Ottenhausen-Meikle," and except for two Army cots the apartment was unfurnished, though there were paintings and rugs—portraits without frames, and large Oriental rugs. Several suitcases piled on top of each other served as a table in the middle of one room.

Ilse explained to us who the men and women in the portraits were: they were all Ottenhausens. It was a proper portrait gallery. Mrs. Meikle, who had a thin white pigtail hanging down her back, waddled after us and nodded when Ilse pointed at the pictures.

"You just have to talk a bit louder, Ilseken," she shouted, "otherwise the young ladies might not hear you! This one here is Ilseken's great-great-aunt, von Austerlitz was her maiden name. That one over here was her husband; he was in good old Frederick's regiment. Here are Ilseken's grandparents, the kind folks. Your old Mrs. Meikle worked for them as a young thing. Ilseken's papa is over there, and his sister, the Countess, God grant her eternal peace. Did you say something, Ilseken?" Mrs. Meikle turned to Ilse and her white pigtail swung back and forth.

Ilse yelled, "No, I didn't."

Mrs. Meikle patted her cheek and shouted, "So many folks, my goodness, and all that's left now is a little Jew child. But don't be sad, Ilseken, I will make you some cocoa now, that will keep your blood warm." Mrs. Meikle waddled across the Oriental rugs toward the kitchen, and her pigtail swung like the pendulum of a grandfather clock.

She served our cocoa in silver cups, setting them on the table made of suitcases. Then we played dominoes and Monopoly. Mrs. Meikle sat on her cot knitting heavy socks. "For the Count, he has it real cold up there," she shouted and looked at us approvingly through her glasses. "It's nice that Ilseken has company," she shouted again, nodding at us.

We went to see Ilse often because the frameless portrait gallery and Mrs. Meikle's endless supply of cocoa had greatly impressed us. The fact that Ilse did not yet know how to talk about men was a necessary evil we had to accept.

The dreamiest man we knew was Hannes Stelzer, the movie actor. We kept photographs of him in our purses constantly. Every day we pored over all the daily newspapers, hoping to find that one of his old films was being shown in some suburb. We saw his Mozart film seventeen times; every single one of his gestures we knew by heart, and we thought his melancholy face even more beautiful under the powdered wig. We poked one another mercilessly until we both had bruises. Seventeen times we walked out of the cinema holding hands and in tears, filled with contempt for all humanity, people who did not understand our lofty feelings and who were content with their everyday blacked-out world.

Susi corresponded avidly with many men. There was Walter, a former schoolmate, now serving with a tank corps on the southern front. There was a staff doctor at Lake Ladoga. There was an Air Force corporal in France. There was a U-boat mate somewhere. She would smoothe her shiny hair and compose love letters, and sometimes I was permitted to read them.

"Of course I don't love any of them," she said, "these are just stylistic exercises. The staff doctor needs a different style than the sailor, and I need lots of practice."

Susi wanted to become a poet and an actress—she was not

quite sure yet which. But to be a poet was simpler for a
half-Jew: to get into an acting school one had to prove that one
was Aryan.

Because of my admiration for Susi my friendship with
Irene suffered. At first I had tried to be friends with both, but
gradually I began to notice that Irene was not really very
intelligent and that her uncle's tavern always smelled of stale
beer. Susi said that Irene's bosom was vulgar.

Irene was still going to Josef Nedoma's apartment, and
she had no idea who Hannes Stelzer was, not to mention
Mozart. I gave up on Irene. When she realized, she was
miffed. "You just watch," she said, "Susi will make a German
out of you." I thought, Irene is really dumb—that's not the
point at all!

My mother looked at me and said, "Why do you always
pick friends I don't like?" Sometimes I felt sorry for my
mother. She was all alone. My father played chess and fiddled
with the radio. And they all were gone now with the transports, the three aunts from Aussig and finally even Aunt Ella
and Uncle Fred.

They left on a day that was so cold that it crackled, and
Uncle Fred looked haggard and bent under his rucksack, and
he was coughing. Aunt Ella gave my mother the key to their
apartment. We were to go there quickly once more, before the
apartment was to be sealed off, and take out everything that
was still of value. My father refused to go. It made no sense
anyway, he said, and it was dangerous besides. What would
happen, he said, if they came to seal off the apartment while
we were still inside? But my mother shrugged her shoulders

and put on her most determined expression. I just had to go
with her; I could not let her go alone.

The apartment was strange and quiet. There was very
little left really except the furniture, and that we could not take
away. But, forgotten on the highest pantry shelf, we found a
small tray wrapped in cellophane, tied with a pink ribbon.
Under the cellophane were Aunt Ella's masterpieces: flowers
made of fondant, and cornucopias made of marzipan, and
chocolate truffles, and lace cookies. She must have collected
over a long period of time, because the baker had always
weighed all the ingredients with such care. Not a single gram
could ever be missing, not once could we taste a single piece.
How long had Aunt Ella hoarded this collection under cellophane and pink ribbon, to have it ready to show to her first
customers in America?

My mother said that now I could eat it all. I tore into the
package impatiently. But the candies were too stale, the chocolate was gray and tasteless, the fillings were rancid, and the
fondant was hard as stone.

But I had not tasted any sweets for so long, and besides,
I could not throw the candies away: they were Aunt Ella's
collection. So I chewed on them for days on end, and each
night my stomach ached.

I was sixteen and almost as tall as my mother. During the
summer I had suddenly acquired a bosom. I looked down at
me and could not recognize myself. Formerly there had only
been bones and hard edges; now there were curves. My
mother smiled and cut the star off her dress to go to town and
buy me some brassieres. I was too embarrassed to do it myself.

But there were no brassieres to be had, the salesladies said, maybe next month, we haven't had any deliveries for weeks. My mother gave me two of her own; they were mended and faded because my mother received no clothing coupons. But they fit, and my mother said, "Now you really belong with the ladies!" At night she told my father, as she always told him everything. My father laughed, and I grew angry at my mother because she gave away secrets.

Whenever it rained, I had to wear my mother's shoes because my feet had grown two sizes in three months and there was only one coupon for one pair of shoes a year. My father said, "If she goes on like this, I'll have to give up my shoes, too." But I was not as unhappy with myself as I had been. When one had a bosom, one could forget about feet that were too large.

Only my face worried me. It was still narrow and pale, my nose was too big, and I had pimples on my forehead. Though I was able to cover them up with my hair sometimes, they still caused me a lot of sorrow. I envied Susi, who had perfectly beautiful skin; she could comb her hair whichever way she wanted. Susi tried to comfort me. "It's because you're still a virgin," she said, and I sighed. Susi's captain had probably been right.

At bedtime I tried to make deals with God. "Dear God," I said, "if you make my skin look better, I will never talk back to my mother again." But God did not want any deals with me. My skin stayed unsightly. So I decided to become a nun; under their black habits nuns wore a white cloth covering their foreheads. But Susi refused to become a nun too, and that made me mad: it certainly wouldn't be as much fun without her. "Are you crazy?" Susi said. "Me in a nunnery? Me giving up life because of your pimples?"

Susi's eyes were happy now, and she was even prettier than before. She walked around singing Mozart arias about sweet longings, because she was in love again. She had given up her captain and now she was in love with a cadet. Every Sunday she went to Milowitz near Prague, where the cadet was attending an officers' training school. On Monday she would be back with dark rings under her eyes and red spots on her neck, and with no homework. Mr. Kohler shook his head. "How can one forget all about irregular verbs because of love?" He laughed when he spoke. He was an elderly gentleman, and of course he was under Susi's spell, too. Tuesdays a letter would usually be waiting for Susi in Harry La-wichka's office, four whole pages, and Susi would read it and then stare out the window and be lost to any conjugating. After a while Mr. Kohler gave up calling on Susi on Tuesdays altogether.

I sighed unhappily. Before going to bed I stared at myself in the bathroom mirror for a long time. My eyelashes were definitely not as long and as thick as Susi's. Maybe that was why no one loved me? On Sunday, when Susi was in Milowitz, I would sit in my room and read Rilke's *Book of Hours.* I would cry because the poem was so beautiful and because no one loved me. I cried because there was war everywhere and because even Hannes Stelzer was at the front now.

My mother put her head through the door and said, "Would you like me to make you some tea?" I said no. It was not real tea we drank now, but artificial tea flavored with artificial rum. I could not stand it, it burned my throat so. My mother drank her tea all alone, claiming that she did not mind the artificial rum taste. Then she sat darning a black-out curtain; it had become threadbare at the place where I hooked it up every night. My father did not want any tea either, he sat in his usual chair in the living room and played chess. He put on his glasses to play chess now, and I felt irritation: why did he need glasses to play chess?

People with cheerful voices were going up the stairs: Hilde Kuchler was having another party. "She's really living it up now," my father said, looking angry. My mother bent even lower over the black-out fabric. Hilde Kuchler invariably entertained German officers. Sometimes they stayed all night. Mrs. Mares, her neighbor on the sixth floor, complained to the janitor about the noise. But the janitor shrugged his shoulders. "I can't do anything about that, Ma'am. War is war!" What he meant was that it would not be very wise to complain about Germans. Mrs. Mares understood very well and did not say another word.

I was glad that Hilde Kuchler at least was having a good time. The officers were always young and very elegant, with soft leather boots and soft caps. They always stepped aside very politely when I met them on the stairs. Hilde Kuchler always smiled at me: she did not hold it against me that my father no longer spoke to her.

Every night I went to the tavern across the street to get my father's beer. Once a man was standing at the fence fidgeting with his pants. Wanting only to pass quickly, I politely looked the other way. But he grabbed my hand and said something vulgar. I slammed the beer jug on his hand, hard, and he let go. Running back, I heard him curse. Breathlessly I came back upstairs.

My father said, "Where's the beer?"

I said, "I won't go there any more!"

My father said, "You'd better tell me why not!" and I screamed, "That's none of your business! I just won't go, that's all!"

My father slapped my face and said, "What a brat!" Then he went back to his chess game.

I sat in the kitchen clutching the beer jug between my knees and shaking. My mother said, "Please go get Papa's beer!"

I said, "I can't!"

My mother looked at me, her eyes full of despair. "You know I can't go there with my star," she said, "the tavern keeper would throw me out. Please go." So once more I went across the street, beer jug poised. But the man was already gone.

The tavern keeper aimed the spigot and let the beer flow slowly and thinly into the jug; the foam had to settle first. I thought, "I'll never forgive Papa for this. What a hero he has turned into!"

The tavern keeper said, "As long as we've got our Czech beer, we can't complain!" He had a mustache and wore a red bow tie.

I was very unhappy. Going back home, I debated whether to throw myself under the tram. Then they would surely be sorry for the way they had treated me. But I decided

against it. I planned to be beautiful in death, just like An-
neliese Uhlig in her last movie. With a tram, one could never
be sure of how one would look afterward. I waited until the
tram with the blue lights had passed before I went into the
house.

Some days later Susi said, "You can't go on like this! You
are getting more and more sour every day." She told me she
would ask her cadet to bring a friend to their next date in
Milowitz. I needed male company now, Susi decided.

It was a beautiful fall Sunday when we went to Milowitz.
Wearing my best pleated skirt, I felt very beautiful. The train
was filled with girls going to Milowitz. Milowitz was a large
training compound.

At the Milowitz railroad station all the future officers
were waiting. The platform was gray with the many uniforms.
I poked Susi. "How are you going to find your Heinz among
all these people?"

She poked me in return. "Helene, you are a goose."

That very moment a gray uniform dashed past me, and
Susi threw herself at it.

I looked around. Everywhere couples were locked in
greeting. I would have liked to watch for a while, because the
sight was even more interesting in real life than it was in the
movies. But Susi was already pulling at my sleeve, introducing
her Heinz, who looked nice and clicked his heels. Then Heinz
introduced someone named Wolfgang who also looked nice
and also clicked his heels. Then Susi said, "I'll meet you back
here for the six o'clock train!" and ran off with her Heinz's
arm around her.

The railroad station had emptied. I looked at the cadet

named Wolfgang, who was meant for me, and both of us laughed. For a second my mother came to my mind, but I really did not want to think of her.

"Shall we go for a walk?" Wolfgang asked. We went for a walk. We had a good time walking and talking. His eyebrows were thick and grew together above his nose. But he really was not my type because his cheeks were softly rounded; Hannes Stelzer had an altogether different look. But the autumn sun was still warm, the sky was still blue, and I laughed a lot and found myself very amusing. I hoped that my pimples would not be too visible. Why hadn't I gone to Milowitz with Susi long ago?

We had reached the forest. Wolfgang put his arm around my waist and said that I was absolutely his type, what a shape. Then he kissed my ear, and I laughed because I rather liked being kissed on my ear. We stopped at a clearing and kissed for a long time, it must have been hours, because the sun made a small half-circle around us. His ears were red like the ears of Josef Nedoma under the blanket, and I rather liked being kissed for a long time.

Then we went farther into the forest. I was sorry to leave the pretty, sunny clearing, but he wanted to go farther. We sat on the moss-covered ground and continued kissing. It occurred to me that one should not be sitting on the ground in a month with an "r" in it; it was September. But we continued kissing anyway. Then I did not like it so much any more because I saw that he was trying to put his hand inside my jacket. That made me angry. I only wanted to be kissed. He said, "Don't be childish," and when he saw that there really was nothing to be done under my jacket, he abruptly tried to reach under my skirt. That made me even angrier: I didn't know the man at all; who did he think he was? I tore myself away and told him so. "Don't be so dumb," he said, laughing. "You only live once." He wanted to pull me close again, but I got up and slapped his face, just as I had seen it done in the movies. Then I turned, my pleated skirt twirling nicely with me, and ran away.

I was lost in the forest a long time because we had gone far from the main path. The underbrush scratched my legs, and my skirt kept getting caught in it. I was angry and disappointed, and suddenly I thought of my mother again: for heaven's sake, what was I doing in Milowitz?

Then I found the path again and ran as fast as I could, all the way to the railroad station. It wasn't quite five o'clock and there was the jerk, sitting on a bench at the first platform, smoking a cigarette.

I hid behind a pile of logs because I never wanted to see the cadet again. I never wanted to have anything to do with soldiers again. There I stayed, hidden, until the six o'clock train pulled into the station, when I had to leave my hiding place and walk past his bench. He called out to me, "Well, are you unharmed, little girl?" I ignored him totally and boarded the train. I was not going to hide from such a character. My mother was right. They were trash.

Susi was still hanging around her Heinz's neck. Only when the conductor blew his whistle did she jump onto the steps. She waved until the Milowitz train station disappeared from view. The train was full of girls again. Some had scratched legs just as I did, and some looked disheveled and sleepy. Sparks flew past the dark windows. Susi was humming cheerfully, and then she asked me how I had fared. I told her everything about the jerk. Susi sighed.

"You are a hopeless case, Helene."

I became angry again. "And you," I said, "You should comb the pine needles out of your hair before you go home to your father!" We did not speak again until we came to Prague Main Station.

In his letter on the following Tuesday Susi's Heinz asked her to bring me again next Sunday. Wolfgang was looking forward to another afternoon with me. But I said that wild horses could not drag me there. I had had it with soldiers. So Susi continued to go to Milowitz on her own.

Once I asked her, "Susi, how about your Heinz? Does he know about your father?"

Susi answered, "Of course he knows!"

Astonished, I wanted to know, "And—?"

Susi only laughed. "He always wondered about me being so sexy and all. So I told him that half-Jews are sexier than normal people."

Once more I said, "And—?"

Susi continued, "What I don't know won't hurt me. That's his philosophy!"

I nodded. Something was not quite right, something or somebody was somehow being betrayed. But perhaps it had to be that way and could not be different. And why should I be worrying about it? I had not thought it up in the first place.

My mother received postcards now, postcards from the

concentration camp Theresienstadt. They were written in printed letters and each could only have thirty words on it in order to make reading easy for the censor. Once a month everybody in Theresienstadt could send off thirty printed words. "My dears," said the postcards, "We are well we are healthy thinking of you how are you." My mother carried the postcards in her handbag as if they were love letters. She read them often, but they did not tell her anything, those postcards. How could thirty printed, censored words tell her anything? And she wrote postcards in return because everyone in the concentration camp Theresienstadt could receive thirty printed words a month. "My dears," my mother wrote, "We are well we are healthy thinking of you how are you." My grandfather was the only one who never sent a postcard. But my mother wrote to him anyway. She wrote, "My honored father, please stay well."

Toward the end of the winter a card came from Aunt Ella. It did not contain even the thirty permissible words. All it said was, "Dear sister, Fred died yesterday."

Then they all began sending my mother their stamps, because everyone in the concentration camp Theresienstadt received one stamp and could have one package sent to him with twenty kilograms of food. They all sent their stamps to my mother because she was the only one of them not in camp. And every time a stamp arrived, my mother wept. She said, "Where can I get so much food? We don't have enough to eat ourselves!"

Then she wrote to Franziska to send all the linen, one set after another. And then my mother ran to the black marketeers, she pressed her handbag over her star and exchanged my grandmother's trousseau for potatoes and flour and sugar, no matter what: the main thing was to get the twenty kilograms together. She was possessed by the thought of the many twenty-kilogram packages she had to send. She made long lists: "Two sheets, half a pound of margarine, to Aunt Regina."

My father said, "If they catch you, they'll lock us all up."

My mother said, "I know, but I can't let them down. They're relying on me, I'm all they have." My father exchanged his wristwatch for two pounds of bacon to be added to my grandfather's package.

My mother rounded up three kilograms of tomatoes; they were fresh and not too ripe. For a long time she debated whether to include them in Uncle Fritz's package. Finally she did, because she had nothing else to complete the twenty kilograms with. But Uncle Fritz wrote on his next postcard, "Please not to send tomatoes. They were ruined." "They were ruined" had been crossed out by the censor. But we could still decipher it under the pencil scratches. My mother was in great anguish. That night she could not sleep: she could not help thinking how disappointed Uncle Fritz must have been, and how the mashed tomatoes must have spoiled the other things in the package.

Once a month Aunt Annel came for a visit. She brought us her butter rations. All Germans in Prague received special butter rations every month, and Aunt Annel said, "I don't care for butter anyway, just send it to them, child. And don't say another word about it." Then she sat in our kitchen drinking our artificial tea. She unbuttoned her high shoes and said, "It surely is a day's journey to get to you here, I had to change trams twice!" I almost fell off my chair laughing; Aunt Annel only lived behind the Museum, and to get there didn't take more than twenty minutes.

Aunt Annel shook her head and said, "Don't you laugh at me. When I was young like you, I could dance all night— for two nights in a row! Oh, those were the days . . ."

My mother laughed also. "Our tall Helene does take a long time growing up."

At night my father took Aunt Annel home. He offered her his arm to go down the stairs, and Aunt Annel said, "A perfect gentleman, my boy."

My parents spent a lot of time with the Giacomellis from next door. Mr. Giacomelli came from the region of Bolzano in the South Tyrol, exactly where my father had been stationed as a young lieutenant during the First World War. Both of them knew every single hill and meadow there. I thought back with amusement on those days when Mr. Giacomelli had seemed so beautiful to me, like a young god. He was, I admitted now, rather handsome, but his hair was much too curly, and he was not in the least like Hannes Stelzer. Once I pointed him out to Susi, who said, "Well—maybe he's half-dreamy?" I nodded in agreement. How could I have been so dumb?

Mrs. Giacomelli worked in the offices of the Jewish Community. Sometimes, when there was a lot of work to be done that kept her late at the office, she had to walk home: Jews were not permitted to travel on trams after five o'clock. Mr. Giacomelli worked for a big construction firm. He understood a lot about his profession, my father said; otherwise he would not be holding down such an important job any more.

One night our doorbell rang around seven o'clock when we were just having supper. My parents looked at one another, startled. My father went to answer the door; it was only a little man who did not look dangerous at all. Hat in hand he asked for Mrs. Giacomelli. But she had not come home yet. "The poor thing, she will be walking home again," my mother said and offered the little man a chair. He did not want to talk to us at all. All he wanted was to wait for Mrs. Giacomelli.

Mrs. Giacomelli arrived at seven-thirty. The little man looked at us and said that he would like to talk to her alone. The door closed behind them. My parents sat very still. They had completely forgotten about their supper. My mother folded her hands.

"Strange that he isn't home yet," she said. "He usually gets here long before this." They sat quietly again.

The door opened and closed in the apartment next door. The little man was slowly going down the stairs. On the second-floor landing he blew his nose; it sounded like a drum beat in the quiet hall. My parents sat without moving: they were waiting. Then the door opened once more, and Mrs. Giacomelli knocked at ours very slowly. She leaned against the frame, still wearing her coat with the star. She was white under her freckles as she said, "They arrested Andreas today." Then she began to cry, without tears, while sobs shook her small body. My mother took her by the hand and led her into the living room like a little girl.

The following evening Mrs. Giacomelli knocked at our

door again. She was not crying this time. She had spent the day, she said, trying to find out what had happened and where they had taken her husband. But no one knew anything, or else no one wanted to tell her. She asked my father to go to the construction firm and find out. They would surely say more to a man without a star.

My father took a day's leave and went. By noon he was back. Mrs. Giacomelli had been right, they did say more to a man without a star. It seemed that Mr. Giacomelli had slapped the man from the Gestapo who had tried to interfere with his plan for a new bridge. The man had supervised Mr. Giacomelli for two years, and Mr. Giacomelli had endured his treatment all that time. The man, a carpenter by profession, did not understand the first thing about bridges. But Mr. Giacomelli had endured it until he simply could not bear it any longer. He had lost control, and they had taken him away. Nobody knew where.

Mrs. Giacomelli came to visit us often after that. She never had any news, it was as if her husband had never existed. Then someone reported to the Germans that a Jewess was living alone in a two-room apartment, and Mrs. Giacomelli was put into a transport. My mother exchanged pillow cases for salami and gave it to Mrs. Giacomelli to take with her. Mrs. Giacomelli was quite cheerful. She said, "Maybe it will be easier out there to find Andreas."

But several weeks after Mrs. Giacomelli had left, Mr. Swoboda, the mailman, stopped in to see us. He had a letter for Mrs. Giacomelli. He could not deliver it because the apartment was sealed, he could not have it sent back because there was no return address on it. He did not want to have it destroyed. The letter came from Germany, the address was printed with a blue pencil, it had smudges, and the postmark said "Dachau."

Mr. Swoboda took off his mailman's cap and scratched his head. "Maybe it says something about Mr. Giacomelli—we can't just give it to the paper drive!" he said. He crossed himself, because he had never done anything like that in his long mailman's life, and he handed the letter to my mother.

My mother ripped open the envelope. There was only a dirty piece of paper with the pencil-printed words: "Esteemed lady, your dear husband was shot on the 12th of January, 1943."

Susi and I loved going to the movies. The latest UFA films always played in the Graben moviehouse. We read all the movie magazines and knew exactly who acted in what. There were no longer any new movies with Hannes Stelzer, because Hannes Stelzer was at the front. But there was the new film about Mozart, and Hans Holt was rather dreamy, too, in the leading role, especially in the scene where he reached out to his leading lady and asked her to come to his chateau with him.

We adored Mozart and the eighteenth century altogether. I decided to become a fashion designer or a stage designer. I wanted to dream up costumes for Susi to wear on stage. She would not be called Susi then, of course, but Suzanne Renner. She had a rococo figure, with smooth, round shoulders and a tiny waist.

Our notebooks were filled with designs, powdered wigs

and ruffles and jabots on all of them. Mr. Kohler said, "Dear
ladies, no matter how talented you might be to dance the
minuet—all I want from you are the personal pronouns, nothing more!" We sighed deeply; English seemed very banal.
Who had ever spoken English in the world of Wolfgang Ama-
deus?

We continued dreaming our dreams in the theater: it was
Susi who was the romantic heroine on stage, rather than the
silly lady in the spotlight. Susi was the one who suffered and
died. I designed dramatic costumes for her; all the other de-
signers were poor devils without a shred of imagination. We
alone would conquer the world, Suzanne Renner and I.

We were walking home from the theater one afternoon
after seeing a matinée of Schiller's *Bride of Messina.* The day
had brought the first breath of spring into town, clear and
windy. The flower woman with the first snowdrops was seated
at her usual corner.

We walked arm in arm along the main boulevard, still a
bit tearful. Suddenly a gust of wind tore off my hat, a navy
beret. As it rolled across the street like a merry little wheel,
a soldier picked it up on the opposite sidewalk. A tram went
rattling past and then the soldier crossed over, holding my
beret. Susi was pressing my arm hard enough to leave bruises.
The soldier, a lieutenant, was very tall and slim. He looked at
me and handed me my beret. Then he laughed in a slightly
aloof way. "Something like that can't happen to us," he said.

He was still looking at me, but at that moment another
gust of wind came, and his own cap flew off in a half-circle.
He had to run across the street once more, racing after it. Susi

and I stood there laughing. It served him right, the conceited man. We forgot all about the unhappy bride of Messina. The lieutenant came back to our curb, shaking the dust off his cap and laughing. He was blond and tanned, and he clicked his heels and introduced himself. His name was Gerd Koch. He asked permission to walk along with us.

Slowly we crossed Wenzeslas Square, continuing past the Museum and toward the Weinberg section. "I hope none of our friends will see me," I thought in panic. "Please, dear God, make no one see me, everything will be all right if no one sees me." The lieutenant wore a gold Hitler Youth emblem on his uniform, boys from the Hitler Youth had played in Aunt Klara's garden, and his chest was full of medals. But he did not look at all nasty; he had blue eyes and very long eyelashes, and he was very dreamy. It occurred to me all of a sudden that he was even more dreamy than Hannes Stelzer, and I was deeply startled.

I let Susi and him lead the conversation, while I listened. Susi was going strong, and they seemed to be having a good time. He told us that he came from Dresden—"Oh dear me, we are almost neighbors," Susi said,—and that he had studied chemistry—"That was always my favorite subject, too," Susi said—and that he was twenty-two—"Oh, but you are ancient, we are only eighteen!" Susi said and pressed my arm. She is making me two years older, I thought, and I quickly looked at the lieutenant to see if he believed her. Over Susi's head he smiled at me, confusing me even more—men with Hitler Youth emblems should not smile so pleasantly. I turned red and got mad at myself: why am I turning red like that, I don't have to blush just because of a soldier!

Then he told us that he was only passing through, tomorrow he would be on his way to the front. "What a pity," Susi said, and I breathed a sigh of relief. Then I got even madder at myself. Why was I relieved? He did not concern me at all. Susi was welcome to him, she could do whatever she pleased.

We parted on the Weinberg Hill, and Susi gave him our school address and our names again. She really did not have to give him my name—I did not want to have anything to do with him. He saluted and turned back.

Susi said, "Boy, was he nice. I wonder if he'll write to us? Oh my God! What will happen if I have to choose between him and Heinz?"

I said, "See you tomorrow," and ran off. I could not stand it a minute longer, my heart was beating wildly. I had to walk home because I could not bear anyone's seeing me, not even now. Everyone in the tram would have been able to read on my forehead: that gold Hitler Youth emblem and those long eyelashes, and even more dreamy than Hannes Stelzer . . .

My mother had kept supper warm for me. She asked, "Was it nice?" I stared at her. "What?" She said, "Didn't you go to the theater today?" I said, "Oh yes, the theater—" and then I could not swallow a bite, although we had red cabbage with potatoes, and I usually liked that. Then I locked myself in my room, holding my beret on my lap. I looked at it, shaking because he had held the beret in his hand—boys from the Hitler Youth had been in Aunt Klara's garden. Then I took the beret to bed with me; I laid it next to my face on my pillow, and I could not stop shaking.

I was calmer the next morning. I hid the beret in the drawer underneath my flannel nightgowns. I knew that I would never again be able to wear it. In school Susi asked, "Why were you such a bore yesterday?"

I blushed. Susi looked at me. "You did like him, I could tell right away! Oh, Helene, why are you such a dummy?" Then she hugged me. "When he writes," she said, "you can have the letter. I want to be faithful to Heinz anyway." Giggling, she let go of me and began to sing her favorite aria: "Voi che sapete . . ." I felt myself blushing all the way up to the roots of my hair; I got up and threw my grammar text at her. It landed at Mr. Kohler's feet because he was just coming into the classroom.

He said, "Sometimes I wish private schools could give detentions, too."

During class I could not keep my thoughts together. Vocabulary words buzzed through my head and did not mean a thing. I looked out the window. Each gust of wind out there was my friend—it had the power to make berets roll across the street. I stared outside and heard neither Mr. Kohler's voice nor the voice of Ilse Wagner, who wanted to help me with the pluperfect.

Two weeks later the letter really did arrive, on a sunny morning in March. For two weeks I had told myself, "If he writes to Susi, I will tear up the letter, and that will be that."

Harry Lawichka brought the letter to class during the eleven o'clock break. It was addressed to me, to Helene Richter, and it was the first letter I had ever received from a man.

Harry Lawichka, happy because he had bet on a good horse, said, "Well, look here, look at our dutiful Helene!"

I sat with the letter in my lap and I was shaking again. The letter bore no stamps; instead, it was franked with a round marker inscribed "Front Mail." The sender was Lieutenant Gerd Koch, Front Mail Number 77351. I ripped open the letter. Written from Charkow, Russia, it began, "Dear Miss Richter," and continued, "on my long voyage here I debated whether or not I might write to you. You had not asked me to do so." My God, I thought, the letter is really meant for me, he hasn't mixed up our names. I went on reading. "But perhaps you can forgive the savior of your hat for doing so? I liked your stubborn silence so much."

"What's he writing?" Susi said. "Show me—"

I handed Susi the letter. My eyes were filled with tears. Why did I have to weep just now? I put my head on the school table. The green wood, cool against my forehead, glowed dimly through my tears. Susi said, "Don't bawl!" as she continued reading for me. "Next month I will be entitled to a leave because I have not been home for two years. If you permit, I would like to come to Prague for a short while. We could then keep stubborn silence together, because I like to do that too."

Susi laughed and said, "Your lieutenant has a sense of humor."

I had to laugh, too. I laughed and cried at the same time and hugged Susi. He was not my lieutenant, he had medals on his chest with swastikas on them, but I was crazy about him. I poked Susi and pushed her, Susi poked me back, but I was taller and stronger than she. We giggled and finally landed on the floor, bringing us to our senses. "I have at least five new bruises," Susi said, sulking and pouting. "Heinz won't believe me when I tell him that you gave them to me." Then we giggled some more. But by the time Ilse Wagner came back from the lounge, we were our serious selves again.

I had to write a letter in reply, and I had no idea how to begin. How did one address lieutenants? "Dear Lieutenant" sounded funny. "Dear Mr. Koch" would not do either. "Beware of me because I am a half-Jew. Sincerely yours, Helene Richter." I knew that I would never be able to write that. I was sixteen and it was spring, I did not want to think of my mother, I was shaking when I thought of him, what concern of mine were all the racial laws?

"Just write, 'Dear Gerd, love and kisses'!" Susi said, shrugging her shoulders impatiently. "You really are a silly goose, so much fuss about one single letter! What will you do when things get serious?"

"But things are serious, Susi," I said unhappily. I saw Aunt Klara's garden and the boys with their brown shirts.

Susi smoothed her shiny hair. "As long as he doesn't want to marry you, you don't need to be Aryan." Then she began to sing "Deh, vieni alla finestra," pretending to be holding a guitar, just as any famous tenor would do in *Don Giovanni.* I couldn't help laughing again. Susi was right, everything was very simple.

At night I locked myself in my room once more. I wrote: "Dear Gerd, I am glad that you want to come. I will show you Prague, and maybe I will even add some explanatory comments."

My father sat listening to the radio every night. Sometimes Dr. Rechlitz came down, and sometimes my father's colleague, Mr. Kuchera, came over. They would put their heads together, pressing their ears against the fabric of the speaker. Dr. Rechlitz had no radio, he had been made to turn it in, but my father was allowed to keep his once he removed the short-wave knob. They could get a Swiss station, Beromünster, on the long wave. The announcer there spoke a strange German, and my mother explained, "That's how they speak in Switzerland. We always wanted to send you to a Swiss finishing school."

My father always looked cheerful after he had listened to Radio Beromünster. He said, "The battle of Stalingrad, that was the beginning of their end."

But my mother sighed, "It will last a very long time."

I began shaking again and asked whether they had not said something about a city named Charkow. My father said, "Oh no, it won't go that fast, that's in Western Russia." My mother quickly looked at me, but she did not speak.

Later, in the kitchen, she told me that it was forbidden under penalty of death to listen to foreign broadcasts, and that I must never, not with one single word, mention it to anybody. I became very impatient with my mother. After all, I was not a little kid who had to be told such things. My mother only looked at me.

"I just want you to be absolutely clear about it," she said. And I thought, if you only knew, Mama, how good I am at keeping secrets.

In April my grandfather died. "A beautiful, quiet death,"

my grandmother printed on the postcard. "We were all with him." My mother wept for a long time; she had not been with him. She sewed a black band on her sleeve, a grosgrain ribbon she had taken off my father's old hat. The shops no longer carried mourning bands. Maybe they were all sold out.

Toward the end of April I got another letter. This one had stamps on it and a return address in Dresden. Gerd wrote, "I've been home a week now and all I've done is eat and sleep. Four days and three nights on a train without a seat can break down even the hardiest front-line soldier. Please wait for me and be kind."

On a Monday early in May he arrived. He was waiting in front of the school when I came out at twelve o'clock, and there was sunshine in his face and on the silver epaulets, and he smiled when he saw me.

I got so flustered that I jumped down the last five steps, almost falling. Then we stood there looking at each other. We were in everybody's way, and I did not care in the least that Mr. Kohler had come down behind me and saw, and that Harry Lawichka went past, and Ilse Wagner, too, and Ilse Ottenhausen.

We shook hands, and I said, "I'm glad you came."

He said, "I'm glad you are here." That confused me again, but fortunately right then Susi joined us.

"Oh, the lieutenant," she said. "Visiting our town again?"

He assumed his aloof expression as he replied, "Well, one does what one can."

Susi was tactful, claiming that she would have to go home

at once for lunch, although it was Monday, and on Mondays we usually ate our sandwiches in the park before going to the indoor swimming pool. My sandwiches and bathing suit were in my school bag. But Susi was tactful, and I breathed a sigh of relief.

When Gerd said, "Now you will have to guide me," I was still staring at him. He really did have eyelashes like a little boy's, very long, and blond eyebrows.

I asked, "What would you like to see first?" And I felt flustered again because I, too, had without thinking addressed him in the familiar form. It seemed to me it could not be any other way; it was as if I had known him for years.

Once again panic seized me. No one must see me with him, everyone would be able to see that I was in love with him. Dear God, make me gain control of myself, and don't let us run into anyone I know.

I took him to the tram station. The Number One was just pulling in, and we went the way I had always gone, to the end of the line. We stood on the platform, he held my school bag, and I thought of the man with the star whom they had pulled off the streetcar that day, how he had looked back. I thought, if he knew, he would not be holding my school bag, he would run away. I am a filthy half-Jew.

Gerd looked down at me and smiled. He was a head taller than I, and he looked down at me the way one looks when one has found somebody for whom one has searched for a long time. As the tram rattled toward its destination, I was very happy.

Then we arrived at the terminal. The tram turned a loop,

and the driver and the conductor took out their thermos bottles. Gerd said, "Come, you have to have some lunch." We went to a small tavern, where the waitress was very grouchy. I knew why she was like that: Gerd's chest was covered with so many swastikas. All they had were potatoes with gravy, she said. So we shared my sandwich and drank bright red soda. Gerd took off his cap.

"It's almost scary," he said. "The silence here . . ." Then he paid for the soda.

I had never had a man pay for anything before, and I quickly reached for my purse. But then, halfway, I decided not to; Susi certainly wouldn't. He noticed and smiled, and I was embarrassed all over again.

Then we strolled over the meadows of the White Mountain battlefield. The sky curved huge and shining over us. Suddenly I was very talkative. I told Gerd all about the big battle. I knew exactly where the Protestant armies had stood and from which side the Bavarian Prince Bouquoy had arrived. I had always loved history, and my father had once described the whole battle to me. Gerd waved my school bag, he had stuck his cap under his belt, he held his hand to his mouth pretending to sound the bugle, and I pretended to dash off in a gallop. But he caught up with me.

"Please," he said, "let's not play war, not even the Thirty Years' War, not this week. Please."

We walked slowly toward the castle grounds. He put his arm around my shoulder. Frightened again, I thought, "Dear God, don't let it be like in Milowitz!" But Gerd said nothing about my shape and nothing about me being absolutely his type. His uniform smelled good and strange, and I asked what it smelled of.

"Freshly deloused," he explained, which made me laugh uncontrollably. He laughed, too, and I was no longer scared.

We strolled around the little castle which Ferdinand of Tyrol had built for his wife in the shape of a star. Overgrown paths led through the grounds; no one ever came here, and no one took care of it. The trees, moss-covered, grew intertwined. Gerd did not take his arm from my shoulder, and I felt very protected and happy.

He told me that he had only his mother now and a young brother; his father had died during the first days of the war. Now his mother had taken over his father's practice—she was also a doctor—and his brother dreamed day and night of becoming a soldier.

"He doesn't know yet how it is," Gerd said. "I used to be that way, at eighteen, volunteering after two semesters." Since then there had been nothing but war: in France, in Africa, in Norway, in Russia. There had been months with malaria and a shoulder wound in a field hospital near Odessa, and nothing but war again. His face had aged, and his mother had barely recognized him, he said, laughing. He had earned all the medals, one after another, he was proud of them, but they were really nothing special, he said, and shrugged his shoulders. I would have liked to touch the furrows in his face and stroked his hair, too, but I could not do that. So I contented myself with matching my steps to his; I had to take very large strides to keep up with him, and we laughed about that.

Then we sat down in the grass, and Gerd made me show

him my textbooks. He had learned English in school. He laughed about all the crinolines, and he said in English, "It is a beautiful day today, and I am very happy, are you also very happy?" I nodded. He lay down in the grass chewing on a blade of grass. He had closed his eyes, and his eyelashes spread like small upturned fans on his cheeks. A May bug came and sat on his forehead. I carefully took it off and let it fly into the blue air.

Then Gerd picked a daisy and began to count quietly, "She loves me, she loves me not." But he did not tell me the outcome, he only nodded earnestly and took my hand and smiled. All was quiet around us; only the birds behaved as if the whole park belonged to them exclusively.

Gerd reached into his pocket. "I've brought you something," he said, "I almost forgot all about it." The round, red-and-white tin box said "Scho-ka-kola": it contained chocolate. I closed my eyes and sniffed it, I had not seen chocolate for years. "A lady may accept chocolate and flowers from a gentleman," Aunt Ella had once told me. So I thanked him politely, sniffed some more, and was tremendously pleased. Then I put the box away in my school bag; it was not possible to devour something so precious right away. I wanted to give a piece to my parents, and perhaps ration the rest to make it last a long time.

But then Gerd's watch showed five o'clock, and I suddenly remembered my mother. I shook the grass off my skirt, and we slowly walked toward the end station of the tram.

As I was walking upstairs at home, I remembered that my bathing suit was not damp. My heart started beating madly. I ran downstairs to the janitor's floor, into the air-raid shelter, where there was a large water barrel. I dipped my bathing suit into it. Now it looked as if I really had been swimming.

My mother said, "You'll be wanting to eat a whole loaf of bread, after all this exercise, right?" She laughed and made some sandwiches for me.

I said, "It was great today, we'd like to go again tomorrow, may I?" Gerd was going to be waiting outside the school at noon.

My mother said, "If it won't tire you out too much. You're thin enough!"

I replied, "Oh, of course it won't."

She patted my behind. I felt awful for lying to her, and I was shaking, too, because Gerd would be waiting for me in eighteen hours.

"Look," I said, "look what Susi brought me!" I showed her the round tin box, and my mother said, "Oh my God, there still is such a thing as chocolate! Where on earth did she get it?" I pretended to be very casual and said, "Her Heinz must have given it to her."

My mother quickly put the box away. "Why does she have to hang around with soldiers," she said. "Aren't there any other young men? Only housemaids used to hang around with soldiers." I thought of Gerd and grew angry at my mother. I ran out, slamming the door behind me.

My mother came to find me. She hugged me and said, "Don't be mad, I know Susi is German, and all the German boys are soldiers now, that can't be helped. It is nice of her to share with you."

I sulked for a while longer. Then I insisted that my mother must divide the chocolate into three parts, and we all had bread and butter and chocolate for dinner. It was a real banquet, my father said. But my mother ate only one small bite and took the rest to the kitchen. I never saw it again; the following day a package went off to my grandmother, and the piece of chocolate from Gerd must have been in it.

At noon Gerd was waiting, and I barely recognized him because he was wearing civilian clothes. The sleeves of the brown suit were a little bit short. He looked much younger today, and suddenly I loved him so fervently that it almost took my breath away. He carried my school bag again.

"Let's pretend that there isn't any war, shall we?" he said.

I nodded happily, thinking, "Maybe he'll kiss me today. Dear God, make him kiss me today!"

We went to the Savarin Restaurant for lunch. I did not have to worry that someone might see me with him: there were no more swastikas, he was a civilian. We sat in the restaurant garden eating veal with potatoes and cream puffs for dessert—many, many cream puffs, because Gerd had a lot of food coupons. The waiter thought we were very funny: Gerd kept ordering cream puffs, and we ate and looked at each other and laughed between the bites of cream which was made of God-knows-what and was sticking to our tongues.

Then we rode the tram to the star-shaped castle again because Gerd said that it was the most beautiful spot on earth. We lay in the grass thinking up names for all the clouds gliding above us. Once three little boys came by and spied and peeked to see whether there would be something to see. I had often enough done the same with Irene Dvořak: disturbing lovers and spying on them. But we must have been a disappointing sight for the little boys, because there was nothing to see. All we did was hold hands and look up at the sky.

Once, on Thursday, the fourth day, Gerd took my hand and pressed it to his face. I held my breath again and thought, "Now, please, dear God, now." I looked up at him and we stood very still. He looked at me and his mouth twitched, and I gathered all my courage and stroked his cheek. Very carefully and very gently he straightened a strand of hair on my neck, and then we continued along the path.

That evening I wept in my bed. I wanted him to kiss me, why didn't he? Maybe because I had all those pimples on my forehead? He didn't have to kiss my forehead if he didn't like it. The cadet in Milowitz had not minded and Paul Kunert hadn't either, why did he mind, when I loved him so much? Then I was ashamed of myself: how could I think of the cadet and of Gerd at the same time? I wept even harder, and in the morning my eyes were swollen and red.

I had to think up the most far-fetched excuses now to be with Gerd. I had never been gone from home that much at a time. There was no school on Saturday and it was to be Gerd's last day in Prague: on Monday he had to go back to the front. I could not come up with another excuse, so I just said to my mother, "I simply have to go, Mama, I have to. It is the last time, please." My mother didn't ask and let me go.

That day Gerd was in uniform again and I shrank back, because I had forgotten about all that: the uniform and the Hitler Youth emblem with the swastikas. They were all there again. I thought the whole morning, "I have to tell him, I have to." I was afraid. Then I took a deep breath and said, "I have to tell you something, Gerd."

He looked at me and said: "What will you tell me?"

I took another deep breath and said, "I am—I'm not really eighteen, I am only sixteen. Susi lied about my age!" But that was not what I had to tell him, that really wasn't all that important.

Gerd laughed a lot and said, "That doesn't matter at all. This way I'll be able to hold on to you longer, when we are very old." I thought the idea of being very old together very funny, and had to laugh a lot too. But that wasn't what I had to tell him.

I was subdued and worried all morning, and Gerd noticed and tried to be cheerful. In the afternoon Mozart's *Eine Kleine Nachtmusik* was playing in the Bertram Villa where Mozart had lived. We had not been able to get tickets any more, but I knew that we could easily go and sit on the wall. The concert was in the garden. One year ago Susi and I had sat on the wall, and it had been much more fun sitting high up among the leaves, looking down upon the rows of chairs.

In the afternoon we went to the Bertram Estate and walked up the path on which Mozart had walked. The fragrance of lilacs was everywhere, and I thought, "I have to tell him." We climbed onto the wall and found a spot under a birch tree. Its branches hung down on us like a curtain. The rows of chairs were filling up, and I thought, "I have to tell him." Gerd took my hand and put it on his knee, and then he leaned his face against it. I felt his eyelashes on my hand. It was very quiet, the conductor tapped and they began to play the Allegro, and I thought, "I have to tell him."

I whispered, "Gerd, I must tell you something."

He whispered too. "Yes? What will you tell me?"

I took a deep breath. The orchestra was playing pianissimo. I whispered, "I am a half-caste of the first degree." That was the legal term for people like me, my father had told me once. Gerd raised his head and looked at me. He had not understood.

I took my hand off his knee. The hand was poor and lonely without his face, and I pressed it against my body; poor hand. Then I explained. "My mother is a Jew. You can go now if you want to, I'll understand."

Gerd looked at me, he was very pale, and the muscles below his cheekbones were taut; I could see each one of them. The Adagio had started. Please, say something, you have to leave or speak. But please, don't say "What I don't know won't hurt me," anything but that, because I could not forgive you, please say something.

Gerd swallowed with great difficulty. "I must tell you something, too, my girl," he said. "I am in love with you. Do you know what that means?"

I nodded, and he went on. "That's much more important now."

The birch tree rustled and a voice below warned us, "Quiet!"

Gerd took my face between his hands and kissed my eyes. Then he kissed my mouth. I sank into a bottomless happiness, deeper and deeper; the Minuet was now being played. I knew

Mozart minuets were the only music played in heaven. And then he took me in his arms, I felt him shivering. I put my arms around him, and he pressed his face against mine and held me.

We sat embraced, unmoving all through the Allegretto. Even during the applause we did not move. I wanted to stay this way always. Then the garden began to empty, many steps rustled the pebbles of the paths, and many happy voices, and finally some more, singly, and then silence fell. Somebody began to collect the chairs down near the stage.

Gerd lifted his head as if he had just awakened. His fingers touched my mouth to seal his kiss. I looked at him, he was as beautiful as the young Greeks in the pictures in the art dictionary.

He smiled sadly. "We have to go."

I nodded. We walked down the graveled path, hand in hand and very quiet, and we took the tram back to town, very quiet. Then we had to say goodbye, because Gerd's train for Dresden was leaving at seven and he still had to pick up his things in the barracks. I had to go home. We shook hands, and Gerd touched my temples with the tips of his fingers, very gently, and the muscles under his cheekbones were very taut again.

He said, "Please wait for me." I nodded, and he touched my temples once more. Then he went away.

I came home and threw myself on my bed and wept. My mother came in and sat down next to me. "Don't you want to tell me about it?"

"No, not yet."

She got up, took off my shoes, and went back to the

kitchen. I wept and was happy at the same time, and I thought, "Dear God, thank you. Please take care of him for me."

The following day I sat down with my mother, she was just grating carrots for a Sunday carrot cake. If you closed your eyes, it tasted just like nut cake.

I began to tell her about Gerd—how it had begun with the beret and how it had continued. I did not leave out a thing, neither the Hitler Youth emblem nor the swastikas. Everything I told her was most important; I wanted her to know the whole story. My mother stopped grating carrots. She sat down and stared at me. She was pale, much paler than Gerd had been, and her hands were folded in her lap. The tips of her fingers were yellow from grating the carrots. The only thing I wanted to keep from her was that Gerd had kissed me, that belonged to me alone.

But she asked, "Did he kiss you?"

I answered, "Yes, once. Yesterday."

She looked at me again and said nothing. I had not known that a person could be so pale. Then she got to her feet the way old women rise, with great effort, leaning her weight against the table. She went back to her carrots.

I waited for her to speak. She would have to answer in some way. But she acted as if the dumb carrots were the most important thing under the sun. That made me mad. I would not eat a single bite of that carrot cake, not one.

That afternoon I went to see Susi, who had stopped going to Milowitz. Her Heinz was in Germany now. We went for a walk, and Susi wanted me to tell her all about it. I hugged her and sighed, and she said, "Now you at least know how dreamy men can be!" I talked, but there were so many things that I could not tell her about: the way Gerd's mouth had twitched, and about his face when he had lifted it toward the curtain of birch leaves.

Susi said, "But next time you have to sleep with him, that's part of it."

Then we took the Number Fifteen tram to a suburban movie where an old Hannes Stelzer film was playing. All at once I no longer liked Hannes Stelzer. I closed my eyes and remembered Gerd's face under the birch curtain, and Susi poked me in the ribs and said, "You really are a hopeless case, Helene Richter!"

By evening I was hungry. I ate half of my mother's carrot cake at one sitting. My mother looked less pale by now. She even laughed when my father said, "My God, what one has to put up with these days! Am I a rabbit?" But he also ate a piece of the cake, and my mother told him that he had always been too much of a gourmet. I had to look up the word in the dictionary.

The following week a letter arrived, mailed from Dresden. Gerd wrote: "Thank you for those six days. I will love you all my life for those six days, because you have shown me that pure and quiet things still exist. I had stopped believing in anything. And I will honor your mother because she raised you."

At the end of May Harry Lawichka came into our classroom. He was very ceremonial, as if he had put all his money on the very best horse. He announced that the school would have to close at the end of June, because somebody in the Ministry of Education had discovered that he was not a hundred percent Aryan lineage. There were rumors, he said, that all half-Jews would be sent to camps soon.

"Let's hope that I can at least look at some horses through the barbed wire," he said and laughed.

Mr. Kohler cleared his throat, and Harry Lawichka quickly looked at Ilse Wagner, slightly unsure of himself. She was German, and one never knew what one could and could not say.

But Ilse Wagner bent her head over her grammar book. She was no longer in mourning—it had been two years. Once she had told Susi that her parents were after her to come home and get married again because the Führer needed more children. But she still carried her husband's photograph in her purse, and she said that she would much rather stay in Prague, it had a healthier climate. Besides, she was not a machine for the production of cannon fodder.

"Did she really say that, Susi?" I asked. Ilse Wagner suddenly seemed a heroine. What she had said was surely considered high treason.

Susi had been unhappy for a while. Her Heinz had never once written to her from Germany. She said, "Pooh, the great love affair!" For several days she acted like a tragic diva, with a deep voice and a melancholy air. Then she recovered and was the same old Susi again: she had met Werner at the swimming pool. She danced around and sang arias about fickle feminine hearts, and she looked at herself in the mirror and pursed her lips. She had very nicely shaped lips. She threw her arms wide and said, "Oh, I just adore men! Especially when they lose their heads!" Then she proudly looked herself over. "Werner tells me I drive him absolutely crazy!"

In the summer she went to the Sudetenland to visit her mother. Mrs. Renner wrote to me and invited me to come along. I spent long mornings standing in line at police headquarters applying for a passport. But I was refused. Half-Jews don't need passports, the Czech official told me angrily. If they have no valid reason for traveling, they should stay home.

Susi was away the whole summer. I missed her a lot. She had gone on to Munich, where her mother's family lived, and she wrote glowing letters about the Hofbräuhaus and trips to the Starnberger See. She wrote: "How can I be faithful to Werner when there are so many nice men here? Oh, life is heavenly!"

I went swimming every afternoon at the Moldau pool, dozed in the sun, and dreamed about Gerd. Once in a while some young man would try to speak to me, but I was not interested in meeting anyone. I belonged to Gerd; not one of the others could measure up to him—how dare they look at me?

Gerd wrote: "My God, why didn't I kiss you? Now I dream about you and kiss you in my dreams, why didn't I kiss you for six days?" And I wrote: "I dream of you too and want you to kiss me, and you can have all of me if you want me, next time." And he wrote back: "No, my beloved, I don't want all of you and you will have to remind me if I should forget, next time. I will have to leave you again, and I know what longing can do to men and to women. Not until we can be together for good—not until then."

Susi returned in the fall. We registered at a private art school to learn fashion design. Susi said, "If I can't become a famous actress then I want to be a designer with you. Renner and Richter! All the theaters will want us to work for them!"

Because the school was Czech I had to interpret for Susi: she had never learned to speak Czech. But now she picked up the most important words very quickly and spoke with a lot of verve, using her hands and feet as well. Sometimes she would simply hang Czech endings onto German verbs. All the girls understood her; they thought she was a lot of fun. They called her Susichka and liked her tremendously. I came very near to jealousy.

All through the fall we spent our mornings drawing gladioli, first in pencil, next in ink, and finally in watercolors. Afternoons we did figure drawings in pencil, then in pen; by the spring, Mr. Pikar, our teacher, said we might perhaps advance to watercolors.

We much preferred figure drawing to the boring gladioli; it was closer to fashion design, we thought. Our model was a small woman with a tired face and fresh scars on her breasts.

"My dear Olga, you do look like an eighteen-year-old now," Mr. Pikar had exclaimed on the first day before turning to us. "They reached almost to her knees last year!"

Olga smiled in her tired way, we all blushed, and Mr. Pikar laughed his head off; he knew very well that many of us were embarrassed at seeing a naked woman for the first time in our lives.

My figure drawings were much better than my gladioli. Mr. Pikar said, "Good, one hundred times more, and don't forget weight distribution!" It took only a few days for us to become blasé about Olga's nakedness; Susi said, "Even Botticelli could not have done much with that one, the poor thing!"

On our free afternoons we had to learn to sew and to make our own patterns. It was left up to us to choose the place where we wanted to apprentice. My mother went next door, where the fat widow Nowotna maintained her workroom, and asked her to take me on. Widow Nowotna liked the idea; she had a lot of alterations to do, and apprentices were hard to get. So there I sat every Tuesday and Thursday afternoon on a stool, hemming and basting and trying to learn something from the older seamstresses.

Widow Nowotna and her seamstresses loved talking about men while they sewed. They held back a little when I was around, and they whispered things they would surely have said aloud in my absence; even what they allowed me to hear was bad enough. I was ashamed and horrified, and I loved Gerd terribly because I knew that with him it would all be different and beautiful.

My father had subscribed to the opera because my mother told him, "Our girl really should go out with her own family once in a while, she can't hang around Susi Renner exclusively!" But it was not easy to go out with my family: my mother could go neither to the theater nor to the movies nor to a café. She could not go out of the house after eight o'clock at night. And my father would much rather play chess or listen to the radio.

But my mother insisted. "Never mind, let Aunt Annel go in my place." So my father had bought three subscriptions.

We went every other week to see operettas, because Aunt Annel had said, "I wouldn't understand anything else anyway, it would be a waste of money." She was in seventh heaven listening to *The Gypsy Baron* and *The Emperor's Waltz*. Her button shoes tapped in time with the music, and above her old-fashioned feather boa her cheeks were pink like a young girl's.

I said, "But Aunt Annel, this is nothing compared to Mozart!"

And Aunt Annel replied, "To each his own, my dear child."

I usually wore my good navy wool dress with the lace collar, and my father put on his good dark suit. He still looked very presentable, I found, and my mother said, "What an elegant family I have! Go and have a good time."

I knew exactly what she would do while we were gone. She would take in her dresses and her skirts, so that my father would not notice the weight she kept on losing. She always divided everything we had into three portions and most of the time carried her own plate back to the kitchen. Later she would give the food to me or send it to Theresienstadt. She would say, "I don't enjoy it anyway." Sometimes when she looked at me there were tears in her eyes. When she saw that I noticed, she would leave the room. I could remember a time when she would have hugged me instead of leaving the room —before Gerd.

All Gerd's letters were now addressed to my home, and she always carefully placed them next to my lunch plate. But she never said a word. She never asked how Gerd was or what he wrote. I became obstinate. I would not say a word to her either if that's how she wanted it, she was not my friend, she was not being honest with me. Or did what Gerd had to tell me really not interest her at all?

The cards from Theresienstadt stopped coming. From time to time we would still get a note that had been delayed by the censor. But all of them were put into transports leaving Theresienstadt, going to a work camp called Birkenau, near Auschwitz, in Poland: grandmother and the three aunts from Aussig, and Uncle Fritz and Aunt Elsa. Silly Paul had gone off much earlier with my ski boots. And Aunt Klara's parents and Aunt Irma, and my grandmother's brothers and sisters and their families, whom I barely knew.

Aunt Ella was the only one who still wrote from Birkenau, near Auschwitz, in Poland, once a month. "My dear ones, I am well I am healthy, how are you?" Maybe the old people were no longer allowed to write? Dr. Rechlitz said that his parents had never written from Birkenau, near Auschwitz, in Poland, either, and he whispered to my father. My father folded his hands on the table with such force that his knuckles cracked.

He said aloud, "But something like that is not possible in civilized times. They could not do that. Not that."

Shortly before Christmas Gerd sent me his front mail stamp. I had asked for it because I wanted to send him a Christmas package. When my mother looked at the stamp I knew what she was thinking: the stamp looked almost exactly like the ones from Theresienstadt.

She merely said, "You can take some of Aunt Annel's butter and bake cookies for him, we don't need all the butter now. We don't send packages any more."

I jumped up, "Oh good! Thanks, Mama." I hoped she would cheer up. But she only smiled sadly at me. She looked so tired; but I did not want to think about tired faces, I wanted to be happy. Why should I be bothered with sadness?

For one whole day I baked butter cookies, and the whole apartment was fragrant. After supper we had some with our tea, and my father said, "Your Gerd will certainly like these." I was pleased—at least my father understood me. I used my pocket money to buy Mörike's novella about Mozart in Prague. I packed the cookies into a box, added the book, and then took my navy beret from underneath my flannel night-gowns where it had been since that day; I put it into the package as well.

Gerd wrote, "My Christmas Eve was made beautiful by your book. I didn't get too many of the cookies, though, because all my comrades thought they were the best thing they had ever eaten. Later you will have to make them for me at least once a week. And I am wearing your hat under my helmet now for good luck. I only wish I were a medieval knight."

He wrote almost every week. Sometimes his letters were only ragged slips of paper, the pencil markings almost illegible, without much sense, expressing infinite exhaustion. I wept over them, my poor, poor Gerd, please sleep, I will not worry even if you don't write. I thought of him constantly; talking to my mother, watching my father play chess—always

there were thoughts of Gerd. They made me forget the sadness in my mother's eyes and the way the hands of my father
shook, his fingertips yellowed by the foul-smelling cigarettes
that were his ration.

I wrote long letters to Gerd; every night I sat in my room
writing. I described everything I had thought and done during
the day, and sometimes I wrote about the way life had been
long ago: in my grandparents' house with the attic, with the
swimming pool blinking in the sun next door, and with my
father going out hunting when he was still my hero, and with
my mother, not thin and with lines of suffering in her face, but
young and beautiful on Aunt Klara's terrace under the stars.
I wrote happy letters because the thought of Gerd made me
happy. Sometimes he wrote back happily, too; he described
his comrades on the front and his childhood in Dresden. Once
he had had an accident playing hockey, long ago: he rammed
the blade of his skate into his foot. But he would not say a
word about it at home—men should not moan, his father had
said. When at long last he had to confess what had happened,
the sock had already grown into the scar. "You will have a
very hard life with me," he wrote, "because I am very stubborn." In the margin he drew a grim, bearded face.

Once he wrote, "Imagine, two days ago I was on a train
going right through Prague, but you must have been asleep,
because it was three in the morning. Our train didn't even
stop. Now we are in Brescia, in northern Italy, and we have
a lot of time to rest up. It is so beautiful here, trees and flowers
are blooming all around, and I'm beginning to understand
why all our ancestors were always attracted to Italy. Besides,

a year ago today I picked up your hat, do you remember? To think that I might never have found you if that day hadn't been windy! Some day we'll go to Italy together to celebrate."

I looked up Brescia on the map and was happy. Nothing would happen to him there, there was no fighting in northern Italy. His next letter contained a photograph: his shirt sleeves were rolled up, his face was tanned, and he was laughing. It really was almost summer in Brescia. Susi nearly fainted when I showed her the picture. She admitted that Gerd was more dreamy than Hannes Stelzer.

I carried the photograph with me everywhere. At night I put it on the bedside table. My mother saw it when she came in to kiss me good night, and for a fleeting moment she smiled. I thought, "Maybe everything will be all right between us now." But her eyes turned sad again. She turned off my light and closed the door.

On a Friday afternoon in late March, when I came home from art school, I found my mother lying on the couch. She was very pale as she said, "I don't know what's wrong with me, I don't feel well at all."

When my father came home from his office, I warmed up our dinner. My mother was lying very still and did not want to eat.

Susi and I had tickets for *Don Giovanni* that night, and I asked my mother whether she wanted me to stay home.

"No," she said, "No, just go. It won't amount to anything."

My father went upstairs to get Dr. Rechlitz. The doctor

pressed my mother's stomach; she said that it hurt. She cried out, and her forehead was suddenly wet with perspiration.

Dr. Rechlitz said, "I really cannot examine her, but you should send for a doctor at once."

My father called Dr. Klatil, whose patient my mother had been some years ago. But Dr. Klatil could not come; he was not allowed to treat Jews now. He did not want any trouble.

Next my father called the Jewish hospital. But they only asked if he was unaware that none of them were allowed out after eight o'clock—neither the doctors nor the ambulance attendants. My father, desperate, replied, "Of course I know."

I put on my navy wool dress and went to see *Don Giovanni.* My mother was moaning softly. My father sat with her, holding her hand. "Maybe everything will be all right by the time I get back," I thought.

But nothing had changed. Another Czech doctor, who had been willing to come, had wanted to take my mother to a hospital. But when he saw her identity card, marked with the large red "J," he had to cancel the order for an Aryan ambulance. Jews were not allowed to travel in Aryan ambulances. He could only give my mother a sedative, saying, "It looks like an intestinal obstruction. She needs surgery. Rush her to the hospital as early as you can."

My mother was moaning loudly by now, tossing her head from one side to the other. My father sat with her all night, and I sat up in my room. I could hear her moans through the closed doors. But they did not want me with them. I no longer belonged with them.

When day broke, my father called the Jewish hospital

again. My mother whispered, "The child should not be here watching." I went and got dressed; but I did not know where to go—it was Saturday and there was no school. I kissed my mother. Her eyes were sunken and rimmed by large black circles. Then I went next door to ask the widow Nowotna whether she had some work for me to do.

The widow Nowotna gave me a stool to sit on and a piece of taffeta to hem. I pulled the stool to the window. I wanted to see the ambulance when it arrived: my mother had always wanted me to see things and to remember them. When the Jewish ambulance with the yellow star on its side arrived and they were putting my mother inside, I started to cry.

The widow Nowotna said, "Don't cry on the taffeta, tears will leave spots."

My father had also gone in the ambulance. After a while I said, "I think I'll go now." I had been careful about my tears, but the hem had turned out crooked.

I went home and waited there, thinking of Gerd. The dinner dishes were still in the kitchen sink. It was after eleven when my father came back. His face gray, he said, "It was too late." Then he sat down at his chess table, lowered his face into his hands, and cried.

I had stopped crying. I went into the kitchen, washed the dinner dishes, and could not believe it. Yesterday at noon, she had been well. After lunch she had said, "Don't make poor Olga cross-eyed today!" because that's what we did sometimes to annoy Mr. Pikar. My mother always thought that such behavior was not polite. And now she was supposed to be dead?

That afternoon we went to the Jewish Hospital. Dr. Rechlitz led us down to the basement. My mother lay on a wooden bench, naked, her stomach covered with a towel. They had tied her chin with a strip of gauze, making it look as if she were wearing a bonnet. Her face was smooth and young, as it had been that night on the terrace under the stars, and my father bent down and kissed it. I wanted to do the same and touched her hand first. But I shrank back: the hand was like stone, cold and hard. I could not kiss her.

Then my father sent me to Aunt Annel's, and Aunt Annel sat on her bed in her kitchen and wept into her handkerchief. Over and over she said, "Your poor Mama, she's better off. God knows what would have happened to her."

That night I called Susi, who packed her nightgown and her toothbrush and told her father that she was going to stay with me for a while. We huddled together in my bed that night, and Susi whispered, "You have Gerd, be thankful for that, I wish I had had someone like him." Her words finally allowed me to cry, and Susi cried with me until we were both exhausted. Falling asleep, I no longer thought of my mother. Instead, my mind repeated, "Poor, poor Susichka."

Three days later my mother was cremated. She could not be buried because that would have meant burial in the Jewish cemetery: my father refused to have her there. The people at the crematorium did not insist on seeing my mother's identity card. My father probably did not tell them that she was Jewish, though such concealment was high treason. My father did not seem to care.

Because I did not own a black coat, Mrs. Rechlitz loaned

me her Persian lamb. It was much too short for me—Mrs. Rechlitz was tiny—and my legs looked even thinner and longer in the black stockings which Aunt Annel had let me borrow. My father sat next to me in the front row. His shoulders were shaking. Then the coffin, which stood at the center of a stage, also began to shake and to move backward. A curtain pulled shut. It was like being at the theater, except that we did not applaud.

Our living room looked like a flower shop: they did not cremate the flowers but gave them to us to take home. My mother's ashes came in a small urn; the flowers took up much more space. Later we buried the urn in the crematorium grounds, under a young birch tree. My father played chess again and listened to broadcasts from Beromünster, and his eyes were tired.

Gerd wrote, "You will miss her a lot, you are still so young. But think how unhappy she must have been. I wish I could be of more help to you now. I have asked for leave and will probably get it in early summer. Think about how we'll be together for two whole weeks, and don't be sad."

I was not sad, and I did not cry much, I had Gerd. I removed the black grosgrain ribbon from my mother's winter coat and sewed it on my spring jacket. Spring came quickly that year, fat buds sprouted on the trees as if nothing at all had happened.

I went to the crematorium grounds often, and underneath the young birch I would quarrel with my mother. "You did not like him," I said, "and I do understand, but not completely, only half of me understands. You shouldn't have been so angry with me. After all, you went against grandfather's wishes when you married Papa. You should have known how I felt when you never asked me about him, never once. You of all people should have known."

There was talk in school that all private schools would definitely be closed down that summer. All of us would be put to manual labor for the total war effort. My father said that all half-Jewish males had already been put in camps, and that it was only a matter of time for me. I started to make deals with God again. "Dear God," I said, "I will go to a camp gladly, but please don't make me go before Gerd comes, please."

Gerd was in France now, he did not write where. But France was safe, anything was better than Russia. The front there was being revised every day, the Germans said, and every day Radio Beromünster announced new terrible losses for the Germans. "It cannot last much longer now," my father said. But he was not cheerful as he spoke; it seemed to be all the same to him. He listened to Radio Beromünster only from force of habit.

Every day after school I went to Aunt Annel's. She prepared lunch for us now—generally nothing but potatoes and gravy except on Sundays, when there was a piece of sausage. I could talk about Gerd to Aunt Annel, I could read her his letters.

She said, "You certainly don't have it easy, you children. When I was your age, I went dancing twice a week, all I thought about were ballgowns and dance cards. All you have are letters and danger, and maybe a few days of leave. It's all

so sad. I wish there were an end to it all. You know, I read
a fairy tale once, where a good witch comes to a girl and tells
her, 'You can choose to be happy in your youth and poor and
sad and alone in your old age, or you can choose the opposite.'
I don't remember what the girl chose, but that's how it is in
life: either you have it this way or that. And you belong with
those who will have a peaceful old age. I wish it for you with
all my heart."

School ended the first week in June. Besides Olga and the
gladioli, we had also drawn handbags and shoes and jewelry
—in pencil, in pen, and finally in watercolors. The real fashion
designing would have started the following year, but that was
not meant for us. The school was closing, and the names of
students and teachers were sent to the Labor Office.

Then it was June sixth and the invasion began. The announcer on Radio Beromünster told of it in a jubilant voice,
and people on the tram nodded to one another, even total
strangers. I knew that Gerd would not be coming now. "Just
imagine," he wrote, "when things started here, I already had
my pass in my pocket. Two days later and I would have been
in Prague. Please think of me now, you are much in my
thoughts."

That summer Susi went to Munich again. She sent a
happy letter, and on a postcard from a sailing trip to the
Starnberger See, a certain Helmut signed his name under hers
and made a heart around both names; Susi had written "ED"
under his name which of course meant "especially dreamy."
There was no further mail from her for a long time, and I
began to be miffed: had she really forgotten me just because

of some new man? But toward the end of the summer Susi's mother wrote to me. The letter was very short, and I had to read it twice before I understood what it said. Susi, Mrs. Renner wrote, had been killed during an air raid on Munich. Her family's house had received a direct hit, so at least Susi had not had to suffer.

Dr. Rechlitz was sent to Theresienstadt. Mrs. Rechlitz was put into a factory—because now it was the turn of the spouses of Jews, my father said. He himself was no longer counted among that category, so he could keep his job as legal counsel. Mrs. Rechlitz exchanged her high heels for work boots and blue overalls. She left very early in the morning; sometimes I could hear her running downstairs before daylight.

I spent the summer in the Moldau swimming pool, waiting for the Labor Office to catch up with me. But the Labor Office did not seem interested. Its raids were directed only at young men, who were immediately sent to the Reich as forced labor. I no longer made deals with God: they could send me anywhere they wanted now that Gerd would not be coming. I dozed in the sun dreaming of him. All his messages were short and exhausted again. The entire Normandy front was collapsing, said Radio Beromünster. Gerd wrote, "I'm still alive and can't believe it myself at times. Only the thought of you makes me glad."

I thought a lot about Susi that summer. Maybe Helmut had been with her at the end, or some other man. God, you wouldn't let her die all alone, would you? Maybe that is why she had lived so fast, maybe she had known it all along, poor,

poor Susichka. Maybe she had felt that she had to live a lot
before it was all over for her. She had not been eighteen.

Sometimes I visited Susi's father. He was alone now with
his Greek books. I did not know exactly what to say to him.
At the end of summer he was put into a transport because he
was no longer living with the Aryan part of his family: Susi was
dead, and Mrs. Renner was not allowed to leave the Sudetenland.

I helped him pack his suitcase; there was no one else to
help him, and he was very clumsy. Everybody was saying that
rucksacks were certainly much better for transports than suitcases, but he did not have a rucksack. His transport would be
going directly to Birkenau near Auschwitz. Maybe he would
be able to find Aunt Ella out there; Aunt Ella had not written
for months now either. Susi's father gave me a small notebook
of Susi's poems, saying I should keep them for later. Then he
left. He wore his black professor's suit, and the suitcase looked
much too big for him.

In August I finally received the order to report to the
Labor Office of the Jewish Community. On the same day
Radio Beromünster reported that the Allies had liberated
Paris. I went to report for work. The man behind the desk told
me, "Here is a requisition for overalls. You are going to an
armament factory, where all half-Jews are sent now." In a
whisper he added, "It won't be a picnic."

I was amazed that I would not be sent away from Prague.
The armament factory was only an hour's tram ride. The
following morning at six I and my new overalls were at work.

The Hermann Regner armament factory was engaged in producing hand grenades and flashlights for the Wehrmacht. The hand grenades were pressed downstairs in the machine room, and after a week there I would go upstairs to the flashlights for two weeks. The old man to whom I handed the pressed halves of hand grenades shouted, "That's because the likes of you can't stand the noise down here longer than a week!"

The machine room was very large and dark. Every machine was manned by one worker and one half-Jew to help him. Besides handing the hand grenades to the old man, it was my duty to pour liquid into the machine every three minutes, so that it would not overheat. I asked the old man what kind of a liquid it was, it looked like very dirty soap water. But the old man could not hear me, he was deaf. The room was very hot. We worked until six.

The first evening I fell asleep on the tram going home and rode all the way to the final stop. The conductress woke me, saying, "Did you stay out too late last night, Miss?" I had to ride part of the way back to get home, and I did not arrive until eight. In order to be at the factory by six in the morning I had to leave home before five. One minute after six the clock started punching in red. If you had two red times in one month, you had to work an extra week in the machine room.

One day as I carried a canful of liquid from the warehouse to the machine room, a man in a black uniform strutted toward me. "The SS are sniffing 'round here all the time," the deaf old man had said, "ever since the half-Jews started working here." The can was very heavy, and it slammed against my

knee as I walked. I could not make room for the man quickly
enough. He reached out with his gloved hand and slapped me.
I almost dropped the can and spilled all the liquid. Remarking,
"Damn dirty vermin!" he marched on in his black leather
boots as if nothing had happened.

Then the letter from Dresden arrived. My father had put
it next to my dinner plate, just as my mother had always done.
It had come with the morning mail, and it was from Dr.
Elizabeth Koch. I stared at the letter and did not want to open
it. If I leave it alone, I thought, maybe nothing will have
happened. But I knew. I held my hands behind my back. I will
have to open it, I thought, maybe it won't be terrible. But I
knew. "Dear Miss Helene, Gerd has been missing in action
since September. I received the news today. I had promised
him to let you know immediately should something happen.
He liked you so much. Yours, Elizabeth Koch."

The world did not fall apart, nothing moved, the kitchen
light went on burning, I sat at the table, the soup plate still in
front of me and the torn envelope and the letter were in my
lap.

My father was speaking from the kitchen, "Aunt Annel
made us a very nice potato soup today." He came into the
dining room, the steaming soup pot in his hands, and said,
"What happened?" He put the soup pot on the table. I got up
and handed him the letter. The envelope fell on the floor; I
picked it up and went to my room. I undressed. Then I
remembered that I had not washed; I went to the bathroom
and washed and brushed my teeth. Then I went and lay down.

My father came in and said, "It doesn't have to be the

worst. When someone is missing, there is always hope—" I nodded. He looked at me and left.

I looked around my room. Nothing had changed in it. Gerd's photograph was on my night table, his tanned face was smiling at me as he stood in his shirtsleeves. As I looked at the picture, I thought, "Why didn't I feel it? Is it possible that one doesn't feel it?"

Two days later another letter from Gerd arrived. It said, "Do you know what we forgot to do? We forgot to carve a heart into a tree with our initials in it, there are so many of those here. We have to do it next time, I've become as superstitious as an old woman, with your hat under my helmet." There won't be a next time, I thought. But it is not possible, I did not feel it, it just is not possible.

One more letter came from Dresden. Gerd's mother was sending me a letter the commanding officer had written her. "Gerd was in the front lines," it read, "and when we retreated, we realized that he was no longer among us. It is possible that he was taken prisoner. Otherwise we must fear —" I did not read on. I did not want to read on. I sent the letter back to Mrs. Koch, *otherwise we must fear, otherwise, otherwise.* In the night I woke up because somebody was screaming, screaming so terribly, was he alone and hurt, but it was me— only I had screamed in my sleep. Were you alone and hurt, all alone somewhere, all alone, and I didn't feel it?

But even the nights in which I screamed passed. The factory clock went on ticking, you have to punch in, don't forget to punch in, one minute after six it will punch red. One week in the machine room, two weeks of flashlights. Nothing was different, nothing had changed. Only I had not felt it.

Downstairs in the machine room the workers were on overtime. The Czech workmen received extra cigarette rations when they produced a lot of nice hand grenades. The foreman did not even like the old man taking a sip from a bottle of beer. Each sip meant half a hand grenade less, a pinch of tobacco less for everybody, wheels have to keep turning for victory, sweat poured down every face. At noon the factory became quiet for thirty minutes. But ears continued ringing in the workers' cafeteria, they rang over the potatoes with gravy, three days more, two days more, one day, and then the flashlights again, *otherwise we must fear, otherwise—*

Upstairs, where the flashlights were made, was less noisy. The machines were smaller, and they were run by hand or with a foot lever. I was assigned to a small hand press with which to attach black-out lenses onto the black bakelite, red-and-blue adjustable lenses; if you put one over the other they made purple—we had learned as much in first grade. Two out of every three women upstairs were half-Jews. You could tell who they were at first glance, although they wore the same dirty overalls as everybody else: the large family of half-Jews. Upstairs everyone was cheerful, everyone always knew exactly about the last BBC news; Radio Beromünster was much too tame. Some of them were very old ladies, also in overalls. Of course, old ladies were half-Jews too: why had I always thought that all half-Jews had to be young like me?

Even Ilse Ottenhausen was there. I had not seen her for a whole year. Mrs. Meikle had died, she told me. She had simply keeled over one day. The doctor had said that she had

had a piece of shrapnel in her head and that it had been a miracle she had lived with it for almost three years. No, she had never complained, she simply could not hear at all toward the end. Now Ilse lived alone in the apartment with the portraits and the carpets and the suitcases. She was sixteen. She had not heard a word from her father since the twentieth of July, and some of the officers who had been shot had been his friends. No, she said, nobody had denounced her yet to the Housing Ministry for living alone in a three-room apartment. She shook her head disbelievingly and laughed. She was not at all pretty, poor Ilse, her nose looked very Jewish, and I would have liked to be especially cheerful with her, she needed that. But how could I be cheerful?

Marie sat next to me at her press. She was the only one I had to ask whether she was half-Jewish or not: she wore clean white collars on her overalls, and she was not sullen or vulgar. Yes, she was a factory worker. Before the war, when the factory had only produced flashlights, she had been the mistress of one of the directors. But he had fled to England and had left her behind. Marie was waiting for him, she had been waiting for five years. She said, "It will be over soon, and Jan will come to get me, you'll see."

The other factory workers poked one another with their elbows, sneering. "Yeah, he'll come like Saint Wenzeslas, on a white horse, your Jan! He'll come back, but with a wife and four kids, he will! Marie thinks she's the only one in the world!" And Marie pressed the lens onto the black bakelite. She shook her head, and she said, "You will see."

I could bear the days, they left no time for thinking. But

at night, when Gerd's face looked at me from my night table, things were very bad. I could not sleep, and though I buried my head under my pillow, I saw him all the time, alone, in pain, *otherwise we must fear, otherwise*—Dear God, if it is that way, did he at least die quickly? If you made him suffer, if you made him suffer all alone, I will not believe in you any more. You don't care in the least what happens here on earth, why don't you care, why? Do you even exist?

Twice a month I was on night duty. I had to sleep at the factory. Three of us were on duty at any one time. Every two hours we had to bundle up and patrol the factory. It was icy cold, our teeth were chattering, we were scared of the silence in the machine room and scared of the shadows in the yard. But we had to patrol the factory and protect it from sabotage. A clock in each room had to be punched every two hours. We clung to one another; often I was the oldest, and I was seventeen.

One day on the tram I picked up a leaflet. It was old and yellow, and it read: "German soldiers! Surrender while you still have the chance! East Prussia has fallen. The American Army stands at the Rhine. Germany lies in ruins. Surrender, shorten the war, and save your lives." I put the leaflet in my pocket. Surely such news must mean the end of the war? I was breathless when I arrived at the factory, and I showed the leaflet to the others. But they were not as pleased as I was. Marie grabbed it out of my hand, put a match to it, and threw the charred pieces down the toilet. She said, "Don't ever pick up such a thing again! If they found it on you, they would put us all against the wall!" She shook her head. "These children have no sense!"

New posters in all the trams showed a large red claw with long talons about to crush the Prague Castle. The caption read: "Order—or Bolshevik chaos!" Most of the posters had been defaced with the penciled addition: "We are not scared, that's not where we live!" It rhymed in Czech, and everyone knew that the Prague Castle was the seat of the government which cooperated with the Germans. The posters were removed overnight.

Each day was like any other. Was I still alive? Factory, sleep, factory, sleep. Every fourth Sunday I had a day off. How would I celebrate my day off when it finally came, *otherwise we must fear, otherwise?* I sat under the portraits with Ilse Otten-hausen, where nobody cooked hot cocoa for us now. Once Ilse said, "Sometimes I feel like everybody around me is dead. I'm the only one left. It's a terrible feeling." We played dominoes and Monopoly, the apartment was deathly still. I had always been so happy when I won a game. *Otherwise, otherwise*—was it possible that one didn't feel it?

Then the first flower women came to sit on the Graben again, selling the first snowdrops. I could not see them because at five-thirty in the morning when I went past the Graben on my way to work, they were not there yet; and at night when I went home, they were already gone. But my father told me that they were there. The wind was blowing as it had that day two years ago. But I did get to see the spring once in a while because several times a week we had to have an air-raid drill. The shelter was a quarter of a mile away from the factory,

across the meadow. The sun was in my face as I ran to it, and
the clumps of grass were thick and green again. I had always
been so happy about the coming of spring; I had always felt
it like a special present just for me. Now I could not feel
happy.

Fat Mrs. Malechek said, "They'll hit us for sure before we
can even get there!" She was running along with me, and her
old body in the patched overalls was shaking. How beautiful
it would be, I thought, to be able to lie down in the grass and
not move, and maybe even cry. But I could not cry anyway.
The air-raid shelter smelled damp and dirty, the door slammed
shut behind us, the sun disappeared. We sat down on the
ground, as part of the drill.

And one day it was not a drill. Even as we ran across the
meadow we heard detonations. Mrs. Malechek yelled, "What
did I tell you, they'll hit us right here, like rabbits!" We ran
until we gasped, but the bombs did not seem to be coming
closer. The air remained pure even after the all-clear had been
sounded. Only when we returned to the factory did we hear
that the Weinberg Section of Prague had suffered several
direct hits.

"Those jerks," yelled Mrs. Malechek. "Don't they know
where the factories are in this town?" Mrs. Malechek was a
Communist, Marie said, and the Americans could never do
anything right as far as she was concerned.

Going home on the tram that night, I was afraid. Our
house was right under the Weinberg Hill. I saw fires burning
behind the Museum, but no, it was not Aunt Annel's house.
We had to get off the tram and walk, trams had stopped

running for the night. But everything was all right at home, only one window pane had burst. Later, Radio Beromünster announced that Dresden had been destroyed that day. The northern sky glowed a pale orange all night long. Three weeks later my letter to Mrs. Koch was returned to me. It had been rubberstamped to read: "Addressee missing in terrorist air raid." Poor Gerd, I thought, now you don't have your mother any more. How good that you don't know.

One Sunday dawned more beautiful than all the others. The sky was clear and pure, and even before the sirens sounded we could hear the humming. Then we saw them, because we just could not stay put in the shelter. We saw them like tiny specks in the huge sky, in strict formation, moving very slowly, and then we heard the bombs. The janitor said, "If the warden catches us out here, he's gonna blow his top!" But none of us felt like going into the shelter; it was all so unreal, how could one sit underground on one's free Sunday when the sky was so wide and blue?

Then the smoke clouds appeared. They rose very slowly, soiling the shiny blue sky. Mrs. Rechlitz said, "That's the factory district. Thank God we're off today!" The humming grew more and more distant, until it was gone altogether. The sirens sounded the all-clear. By night we knew that the factories had got it this time, because the radio listed the names of the ones that had been hit, the Hermann Regner factory among them.

The following morning I saw the wreckage. I need not have hurried to arrive by six, because the time clock was no longer there. The whole street was gone, leaving only piles of rubble. The workers were happily climbing all over them, noting, "This is where my machine used to be." But all you could see were bricks, iron rods and girders, and mountains of debris. Even fat Mrs. Malechek had to admit that it had been precision work if one considered how high the Americans had flown.

Old Regner was running back and forth, his party button shaking with indignation, and he was yelling at us. "Now we'll start rebuilding. Get going, all of you!" We began to pile up the bricks, but none of us was in too much of a hurry—it was spring at last and it felt like a holiday.

Several days later we succeeded in digging out the bakelite room; there were many boxes with halves of flashlights completely intact, the red-and-blue lenses were not even cracked. But even old Regner would not be able to do much with halves of flashlights, said Marie, and she laughed. We wore gloves, and we covered our faces with scarves because the dust billowed all around. I thought of the Rockies and of Wild Bill Hickok—only the wide prairies were missing in the picture here. Once I had spent a whole summer imagining I was a cowboy. How long ago had it been? That was when everything began to fall apart in the old house. Sometimes, while Marie stood guard, I lay down in the rubble to take a sunbath, because Marie claimed that I looked like a ghost. But I did not really care about my looks, I did it only to please her. At night, when I took a bath, a layer of dust always formed on the surface of the water.

One free Sunday I went to town. But without Susi it was not much fun. The theaters had all been closed down. As an exception, one of Dvořak's operas was given a special performance as a concert, without costumes and without a stage. It was impossible to imagine that the elderly lady on the dais could be a water sprite. Why was she so sorrowful for her prince? Wasn't he alive and standing right next to her?

I was hungry all the time now. My father organized some cornflakes somewhere, and I ate them with a dusting of sugar. But then we were out of sugar for my father's coffee substitute. When the cornflakes were all gone, Aunt Annel gave us a pound of onions, and we ate those, browned in substitute fat, with dry bread. My father did not say anything more about having to put up with things: he was no longer a gourmet.

We began to notice that the black uniforms that had always guarded us at work appeared less and less frequently. There would be whole days when none would show up at all. Toward the end of April they were gone altogether. And the day came when even old Regner, who had yelled so much about rebuilding, was not to be found anywhere. "The rats are leaving the ship," Marie said.

The lilacs began to bloom in early May. They bloomed everywhere, the whole town was filled with their fragrance. Never before had they bloomed so lushly. Everyone talked about their beauty.

One day the tram stopped at the railroad station. People were running toward the station from every direction. Even the conductress and the driver got out and started running, nobody really knew why. The conductress's money bag rattled with every step. I got off and ran too, although I was tired and dirty.

A train of cattle cars was standing in the station, SS men with pointed machine guns before it. They pointed their guns at us and shouted "Halt!"

No one moved. We stood staring at the train. The conductress's money bag was silent, and the only sound was that of deep breathing. We all stared, mesmerized, because the cattle cars were full of people; the doors were open, and we could see them. But they were not really people, they were skeletons in striped suits, with numbers on their chests, Uncle Rudolf, skulls. They were alive, they were standing there, one of them moved his arm in greeting. A skeleton trying to wave with a bone.

Then the SS men with the machine guns started marching in a line toward us, shouting, "Get out of here!" We pressed through the station door back into the street. A woman next to me started weeping. The conductress's bag was still quiet, no one breathed hard any more as all of us went back very slowly. We boarded the tram again and continued on our way, and the man next to me said, "That's how they're sending them back, the sons of bitches," and the man across the aisle said, "I didn't believe it when the BBC announced it." Then no one spoke at all. But the silence was not because they were cautious, the way they had been all those years. They were quiet because there simply was nothing more to say.

The following day people all over town began to tear down the German signs. They tore them off shops and off tram cars, and they decorated the shops and the trams with sprigs of lilac. On Saturday morning my father ordered, "You'll stay home today. There will be a lot happening today, and I don't want you outside."

It seemed very odd to be at home on an ordinary weekday. I tried to clean the house a little. The apartment had been neglected, though a cleaning lady had been assigned to us because we were a "motherless household." She did not clean well at all. When the war is over, I thought, I will have to start cleaning house. When grandmother and Aunt Ella and all the others come back, the apartment will have to be spic and span, they will surely want to stay with us for a few days. For a long time I sat looking at Gerd's picture, Gerd with a smile and in shirtsleeves. If I didn't have the photograph, I wouldn't remember how you looked. All we ever had were those six days. Your arm on my shoulder, I can still feel it sometimes, but I wouldn't know how you looked anymore.

At noon the shooting began, single shots here and there. The radio was deathly quiet. My father reported that the town had gone mad, someone should try to pacify both sides, he said, it would never work out in this mad and angry way. He was hoping the Americans would arrive soon, only their arrival could prevent bloodshed. They had already reached Pilsen, he said.

Then they began to call for help on the radio, in English and in Russian. The janitor came and said that we would have to go to the shelter; the Americans were not coming, and a tank division of the SS had decided to make a last stand in Prague. As I picked up my suitcase, I heard something click close by. Suddenly the chest of drawers had a small hole where there had been none a second earlier. A shot had gone through the window frame into the chest of drawers. There it rested, a minuscule silver bomb.

We stayed in the shelter late into the night. The radio was begging for help in English: "The Germans are shooting women and children here, where are you, please come and help us!" People in the shelter were turning to look at Hilde Kuchler and at my father, who were both Germans.

Then we went back upstairs. Mrs. Rechlitz said that it certainly would be more comfortable to die in a warm bed than in the musty shelter. My father's eyes frightened me. I woke up several times during the night to hear him walking through the apartment. The sky above Prague was very red, and I heard my father muttering, "It can't happen this way, it can't, not after all that waiting. There has to be a bridge."

Next morning he told me, "I have to go. It's no good anymore just keeping out of it. I can't let them kill one another like this."

I objected. "But you have a German accent, Papa," I said. "How will they know that you are not a Nazi?"

But my father shrugged his shoulders. "I have to help. They have to negotiate instead of killing each other. Maybe everything is not lost yet."

My father left. I snuck out the door after him and watched him go. He walked quickly, keeping close to the house walls, his hands in his pockets. Soon I lost sight of him.

When Mrs. Rechlitz heard that my father had gone out, she looked worried. "He should not have done that," she said. "Here we all know him, nothing would have happened to him here." Mrs. Rechlitz's face was white, and she had forgotten to put on lipstick. The radio had announced that an epidemic of typhoid fever had broken out in Theresienstadt, and Dr. Rechlitz was still there. The Americans had not come yet. It took only three hours to get to Prague from Pilsen—where were they?

At night the sky was red again over the city, and the radio said that the SS had put whole blocks on fire, as well as the old City Hall. And then the radio exhorted, "Kill them, kill the Germans wherever you can find them, kill them all, every man, woman, and child!" I shivered. People in the shelter were staring at Hilde Kuchler, the only German in the house now. I thought of my father and of his German accent and of the fact that he had no proof that he was not a Nazi. How would they believe him when they had killing on their minds?

The following day, as I was looking out the living room window waiting for my father, I saw a man with a gun running across the meadow where the sheep had always grazed. He looked like wild Rudi playing soldiers. The man fired as he ran, who was he firing at? Then I saw a flash come out of a window on the other side. The man threw down his gun and fell. I waited for him to get up again, but he did not get up. At night, women carrying a white flag came and took him away. The next day they brought flowers and put them down on that spot, a bouquet of lilacs.

Then the radio said that the Russians were marching on Prague. They would arrive tomorrow. They had had a long journey, all the way from Berlin, the radio said. But the Americans had been much, much closer: why had the Americans not come? "The Western allies always left us to stew," said the janitor. The sky was red again over the city that night.

Three men in the uniforms of Revolutionary Guards came to our shelter and asked for Germans. People pointed at Hilde Kuchler, and the men ordered, "She's coming with us." Hilde Kuchler smiled at me in passing; she still had blond curls on her forehead. One of the men went upstairs and picked up her radio. They probably needed it to make up for all their trouble. They came back once more and asked, "Is that all now?"

The janitor said, "There is a radio at the Richters'."

I went upstairs with them and gave them my father's radio. It was true, it was a German-owned radio, and they probably needed that one also to make up for all their trouble. The man looked at me and said, "What about her?"

Mrs. Rechlitz stepped in front of me. "You leave her alone," she said. "Her mother was a Jew."

One of the men sneered. "They were collaborators too, those Jews!"

Mrs. Rechlitz said, "You go to hell!"

The man scowled angrily at her. "You, sweetie pie, have a German name too!" Then he left.

Mrs. Rechlitz would have jumped at him if he hadn't gone, she looked so angry.

On the following day the Russians arrived. We heard the rejoicing on the radio, and then they said that the war was over now, our Russian brothers had saved us. Why had they not allowed the Americans to save us? The war could have been four days shorter for us.

Then I waited for my father. But he did not come home. I wanted to look for him, but Mrs. Rechlitz said, "I'd rather you stayed home now. The Russians are still celebrating like wildmen." A quarantine had been announced in Theresienstadt, but Dr. Rechlitz had sent a radio message that he was well.

I waited for my father and for grandmother and for Aunt Ella. A newspaper had been published and had written about extermination camps and gas chambers. I thought, "But somebody has to come back, one of them has to, they can't just all be dead." But then I remembered the skeletons in the cattle cars at the railroad station, and I remembered my mother's eyes. Had she known?

And again I waited. One day Mr. Kuchera arrived. He was my father's friend, and they had often listened to Radio Beromünster together. Now he also wore the uniform of the Revolutionary Guards. "Come with me," he said, "I have found your father in the Weinberg School."

We walked up the Weinberg Hill. I wanted to know what had happened. Mr. Kuchera did not speak for a long time; his legs were very thin and he was walking very fast, I could barely keep up with him.

Several blocks later he said, "Your father stood on a barricade, in the midst of all the shooting, and he spoke about reconciliation and about bridges between Czechs and Germans, in the middle of the revolution he did that." Then Mr. Kuchera fell silent again. I had trouble following him, he walked so quickly.

"I saw him," he said, and his voice sounded strained. "I

saw him. The Germans were shooting at him and the Czechs were throwing cobblestones at him, there was a lot of confusion. Now I've found him again, in the Weinberg School."

Then Mr. Kuchera was silent once more. We stepped over a mountain of cobblestones which had been ripped out to build tank barricades. Maybe they were the same ones? When Mr. Kuchera spoke again, he said, "You will have to be very brave, he is not well. He should be in a hospital, but the hospitals don't take Germans. I tried." Then he gave me a swift glance. His hands were clenched deep in his pockets, and he was walking very quickly.

The Weinberg School had been turned into an internment camp. The Germans were sitting on the hallway floors and in the classrooms, there was not enough room for all of them, and Revolutionary Guardsmen with machine guns were posted at every door. On one wall a large lithograph showed Jan Hus before the Council of Constance.

They let Mr. Kuchera and me pass through. We stepped over people dozing and people sleeping, all the children were crying, there was a stench everywhere. My father was lying on a bench in classroom 3-A. His shirt was bloody, and he was moaning. I stroked his hand, it was very hot, and he opened his eyes. His eyes were no longer frightened. He opened his mouth, and a thin stream of blood trickled from one corner. He smiled at me. "Helenka. Be good." Then he closed his eyes again, his face had turned white. There was blood on his pants as well. Someone in the corner said, "He'll die today for sure. Then we'll have more room."

Mr. Kuchera took my hand and led me outside. "He

won't last much longer," he said. "He wanted to see you."
Then he let go of my hand and slammed his fist against a wall.
"What a disgusting business, what a sickening business, our
Revolution!"

As he walked me home, he asked, "Do you have any
money?"

I said yes, I did, my father had been paid just last week.

He said, "I'll come again to see if you are all right."

I nodded, and said, "Yes. And thank you."

The nights were always filled with shooting now and
screams and singing. People huddled together and whispered,
"The Russians are celebrating." Mrs. Rechlitz said, "Just
don't ever open the door at night to anybody!" During the
daytime, she said, I could go to town on my own. I wanted to
visit Aunt Annel, I had to know what had happened to her.

But Aunt Annel was not there; her apartment door was
sealed just as Aunt Ella's had been, except that this seal pro-
claimed, "Confiscated for the Republic." I stood there, uncertain what to do next. Aunt Annel had not divorced a Jew, as
had Hilde Kuchler. She had given her German butter to us
all those years so we could send it away. She had been the only
one of my father's family to accept my mother with love. Why
was her apartment confiscated now for the Republic?

I stood there and didn't know what to do. Then the
janitor's door was opened downstairs. The janitor's wife came
up, wearing a blue bathrobe with torn pockets. She whispered,
"They shot your aunt, the Revolutionary Guards did. Right
here in front of the house they shot her, on that Saturday they
did, because the SS was also shooting people." She patted my
arm and went back downstairs.

I went home. It was all right. The Republic would clear out Aunt Annel's kitchen, which had been so full of secrets. It would do it in the same way the German Reich had cleared out the attic of my grandparents. An eye for an eye and a tooth for a tooth. It was all right.

Once I saw a large column of German prisoners of war. They dragged past our house, some of them wearing dirty bandages, and a large cloud of dust hovered over them. *It is possible that he was taken prisoner, otherwise—* People watching from the sidewalk spat at them. Women were doing the spitting, they had received extra cigarette rations for producing hand grenades. Now they were catching up on the spitting. A man said, "Leave them alone, look at them, they're all poor devils!" The women threatened the man with their fists and screamed at him, "We'll do away with the likes of you, too!"

When the new ration cards were handed out the following month, I had to return the ones for my father. They had issued some to him, but he was dead now. The ration cards were just like the ones my mother had always received: instead of *JUDE JUDE* they had *GERMAN GERMAN* printed all over them. But I could go and return them because my father was dead.

The town was dusty; summer had come suddenly. The lilacs were wilted. Red flags hung everywhere. Men with white swastikas painted on their backs were clearing away the rubble by the side of the road. A Revolutionary Guard stood over them with a machine gun. When they had loaded the cart, the guard harnessed one of the men to it and prodded him with a whip. When the man did not take off fast enough, he was beaten as a horse would be whipped by a mad driver. The guard ran alongside with his machine gun, whip in hand, laughing. Good that my father is dead now, I thought. Tricolored Czechoslovak flags hung next to the red ones.

In June Dr. Rechlitz returned from Theresienstadt. He was haggard and his head was shaved, but he was hale and healthy, he said. Mrs. Rechlitz wore lipstick again and very high heels, her eyes sparkled and her dimples were deep and happy. I went upstairs every day to have my meals with them.

Dr. Rechlitz said, "In the fall you can go back to school, Helenka, and maybe you can exchange the large apartment for a small one. You are young and healthy, things will be all right for you. You don't know how fortunate we all are because we are still young and well."

I did not want to give up the apartment as long as there was a chance that someone might come back. I went to the crematorium grounds often. The young birch had grown since the previous year, and a plaque under it gave my mother's name, Marie Löwy-Richter. The crematorium people had wanted to remove the plaque, the name had seemed too offensively German. It took me a long time to persuade them to leave it. I had to show them my mother's identity card with the red "J" which meant Jew and the yellow star on my mother's winter coat. Only then did they decide not to tamper with the spot under the birch tree.

I no longer argued with my mother. I understood now why she had had such sadness in her eyes. Nobody was coming back. It was useless to wait, nobody was coming back. It was useless to wait, nobody would ever come back again. They were all dead. She had known it all along, from the very beginning. She had been alone with her knowledge, and I had been of no help to her. How should I have helped her, when all my thoughts were with Gerd, in love with Gerd? I had not belonged with her. But now she had my father with her again, and maybe he would be able to persuade her to forgive me.

I went to visit Marie. But she had aged suddenly, and she did not wear her white collars any more. Her Jan had returned from England, but fat old Mrs. Malechek had been right: he had returned with a wife, with an English wife. Marie shrugged her shoulders. I had always thought that she could not be much older than I. But she was much older, her forehead was tired and furrowed, and she said, "I knew it, too, deep down and in secret. Six years is too long."

I went to visit Ilse Ottenhausen. But the sign on the door no longer read "Ottenhausen-Meikle." There was a strange name there now. I ran downstairs to make absolutely sure that I was in the right house. Then I ran back up and rang the bell. A disheveled woman opened Ilse's door. Behind her back I could see one of the portraits, and I asked for Ilse. But the woman said, "How should I know where all the Huns are, I hope they all went to hell!" Then she slammed the door in my face.

One day I met Irene Dvořak. She was very pregnant. When I said, "How nice, and what's your name now?" she replied, "Nice, my foot." She had a hard mouth which I had never noticed before, and she said, "He didn't want to marry me, that bastard Nedoma. But he had to. And once the brat is born, I'll show him what I can do!" She laughed, but her eyes were cold. She gave the eye to a young man who was just passing by, and the young man turned several times to look at us.

Then the trains were running on schedule again, and I could take a trip to see the old house on Prague Street. Mrs. Rechlitz gave me a chocolate bar to eat on the train, English chocolate, called Cadbury's. I could not eat something so precious right away, maybe a small piece every day. Cadbury's. The last chocolate I had tasted had been called Scho-ka-kola. But that had been long ago, a long time ago.

The begonia baskets were still hanging above the platforms. The brickyard was across the tracks, and so was the old thread factory. Main Street looked just as it always had; only the dimensions had changed—everything looked smaller than I remembered. I knew none of the people, not one of them. Where would I go first, to the old house or to visit Franziska?

I decided to see Franziska, because I wanted someone to talk to. I turned left. At once I came to the development near the sugar plant. In my memory the way had been much longer. Franziska was in her garden, hanging up the wash. I called to her.

For a second she stared at me uncomprehendingly, then she dropped the wash and the clothespins and ran toward me. She was round and friendly and very soft, and she was bawling again. Franziska had always liked to bawl, and I told her, "You must stop now, Franziska, or I'll start, too."

Then she took me into her kitchen, where the floor was scrubbed bone white. I said, "But I'll track in dirt," and she said, "Do you have any idea what it looks like when my men get home?"

After she made coffee, she asked, "And how is your Papa?" Of course, she did not know yet. My father had written to her about my mother, but she did not know about him. I told her. She sat very still and wiped her eyes with her apron. "Dear Lord," she said, "dear Lord. There is no end to it."

Then she composed herself and poured the coffee. She apologized because there was only bread and butter to go with it. "You should have written that you were coming! Nothing lasts in this house, with those three hungry men!" I drank Franziska's coffee and ate her bread and butter. The food tasted wonderful. The butter still had tiny droplets of water in it, and they burst when I spread it with my knife.

Franziska was telling me about the gravestone. My grandfather had had a gravestone made before they went away, with his and grandmother's names and their birthdays, and he had bought a lot for it in the municipal cemetery. "You only have to add the death dates, nothing else," Franziska said. "The stonemason will do it for free, and the town will take care of the flowers and of the planting." Then she cried again. I nodded. So my grandfather had known, too. He had known just as my mother had known. There was a gravestone. But where was his grave? And where was grandmother's grave?

Franziska had stopped crying. She began telling me about the German refugees who had lived in the house during the war. "And now," she said, "now there are people in it who had returned from Auschwitz. But they know nothing about your family, the mayor has already questioned them. I wish

you wouldn't go there. You won't recognize the house."
Then she whispered, her eyes filled with horror, "They live
like animals there, God knows what kind of people they are.
I wish you wouldn't go."

But I insisted, "That's why I came, Franziska."

Franziska put away the coffee mugs. "I'll give you some
of the butter to take with you, if you like it so much. We have
plenty." She hugged me. "You should get married soon," she
said. "to a decent man, and have children. Then you'll have
a family again, and things won't be so terrible any more." I
nodded, just to please her. Why was I nodding? Gerd was
dead too.

Franziska walked with me as far as the road. She wiped
her eyes with the corner of her apron and waved with the
other hand.

The trees in the park across Prague Street were taller
now. The silver firs at the garden gate almost reached the roof,
and they shivered slightly. The garden gate stood open, and
the lawn was an expanse of weeds. The last fluffy dandelion
balls stood guard where grandfather's strawberries had once
been. Behind the house, between the bed of rhubarb and the
currant bushes, lay a pile of decayed wood with traces of green
paint here and there: my lawn swing.

I went up the three steps to the glass veranda. The panes
were cracked and broken. The front door, which had been
yellow, was weathered-looking, and the brass had turned
black. How seldom had I ever had to ring the bell here: there
was always someone waiting for me, there was no need to

ring. I barely knew how to ring. I shrank back when I heard
the peal.

Nothing moved in the house for a long time. Then someone shuffled through the hall, the spyhole was opened: how
often had I played with that spyhole? An eye was looking at
me. There was quiet for a long time. Then the door opened
a crack, the chain was latched: how often had I played with that
chain? A man's voice said, "Yes?" and I said that I used to live
here a long time ago, and would they let me come in for a
minute to see the house again?

The man came out from behind the crack. He wore a
black hat and a long black coat. He shook his head. He had
not understood.

I repeated my request, in German this time, and very
slowly. He seemed to understand. He motioned with his hand
and closed the door again. After a while he opened it, but he
had forgotten about the chain. He had to close the door once
more before he could finally open it all the way.

He gestured for me to come in. I entered. The hallway
floor, which had always been so shiny and where everyone's
footsteps had resounded, was covered with ashes and charred
logs. The campfire was at the center of the hall. The room
smelled of humans and of animals. Two goats peeked out of
the pantry; a board had been nailed to the door frame to keep
them in. Chickens cackled in the kitchen.

And then they came out—from the parlor and through
the dining-room door, and down the stairs which were no
longer covered with yellow-red plush: men with black hats,

four, five, six of them, and one woman. The oldest man's beard was white; he also wore a black hat and a long black coat. He was bent over: had my great-great-grandfather looked like this when he came to town with his handcart? The oldest spoke, in Yiddish, "What does the child want here?"

And I told them that I had lived here a long time ago, and that I had only come to see the house again. I spoke very slowly. I wanted them all to understand me, I was afraid of them. They were all so quiet. They stared and were quiet.

Then one of them moved, he pushed up his coat sleeve and showed me his arm. A number was tattoo on the skin that covered the bone. Then all of them pulled up their coat sleeves, and all of them showed me their bone arms, even the woman, even the oldest among them. All wore numbers on their arms, and all were so quiet as they looked at me.

Then the oldest spoke. He said, "Go away, child, and don't come back. Don't disturb us. You don't know, you haven't seen. You haven't suffered. You haven't endured. We are the last. Don't disturb us."

I nodded and gave a final look around. The pale square with the nail above it was still on the wall. I handed Franziska's package of butter and Mrs. Rechlitz's chocolate, Cadbury's, to the oldest. He accepted the offerings and bowed. All of them bowed to me, even the woman.

I went out, down the three steps. Carefully I closed the garden gate behind me. The silver firs were shivering slightly.

On the platform the begonia baskets rocked quietly to and fro. The train for Prague left before darkness came.